The Theory of Rings

The Theory of
RINGS

Neal H. McCoy

Gates Professor of Mathematics, Smith College

THE MACMILLAN COMPANY, NEW YORK

COLLIER-MACMILLAN LIMITED, LONDON

Fifth Printing, 1968

Library of Congress catalog card number: 64–12170

THE MACMILLAN COMPANY, NEW YORK

COLLIER-MACMILLAN CANADA, LTD., TORONTO,
ONTARIO

Printed in the United States of America

To my wife, Ardis

Preface

ALTHOUGH COMPARATIVELY little knowledge of the actual content of abstract algebra is assumed as a background, this little book is designed for students who have had at least an introductory course in the methods and concepts of that subject. It is hoped that part of the material here presented will be suitable for use with graduate or advanced under-graduate students as a supplement to that portion of ring theory which is introduced in the usual course in abstract algebra. Also, depending upon the level of the students, the entire book might be used as primary text material for a one-semester course on the theory of rings.

A glance at the table of contents will reveal the scope of the book. Some of the topics have been included because of their fundamental importance; others, at least to some extent, because of personal prefer-ence or for what seemed to be good pedagogical reasons.

A number of notes, some of them of a mathematical nature and others of a bibliographical or historical nature, are collected at the end of the book. I apologize in advance to those authors whom I may have un-intentionally slighted in these notes. I have also included hints or actual solutions to certain selected exercises. Of course, a conscientious student will try these exercises before looking at the hints and, in some cases at least, he may very well find simpler solutions than those suggested!

It may be worth pointing out that, except for parts of the first three chapters, there is little overlapping either in content or in approach with the material of my Carus Monograph, *Rings and Ideals*, which was published some fifteen years ago. For one thing, the reader of that book was not assumed to have any previous knowledge of the concepts of abstract algebra. Moreover, the theory of rings has itself been developed at a rapid rate in the intervening years. As a matter of fact, several of the results presented here were unknown at the time that book was written.

A substantial list of authors will be referred to in the notes, but it would be unthinkable not to emphasize the importance of the contributions of Professor Nathan Jacobson to the theory of rings, as well as of his various expositions of that theory. In particular, his monumental book, *Structure of Rings*, will no doubt long remain the standard reference work on structure theory.

It is a pleasure to express here my appreciation to my former colleague Professor R. E. Johnson, with whom I have had many discussions on ring theory over a long period of years. He has been for me a source both of information and of inspiration. Moreover, he read the first six chapters of the present material and made several suggestions which have been incorporated in the text or in the notes.

Finally, I am greatly indebted to my long-time friend and collaborator, Professor Bailey Brown, who gave the entire manuscript a most careful and detailed reading. He made a large number of suggestions which have considerably improved the exposition and, in addition, he was kind enough to assist in the tedious task of reading the proofs.

NEAL H. McCoy

Contents

The Theory of Rings

CHAPTER I

Examples and Fundamental Properties of Rings

IN THIS CHAPTER we shall give a number of basic definitions, state several fundamental properties, and give a few examples of rings which may be new to the reader. Other examples will be given from time to time in the sequel. Part of the material of the present chapter will appear almost in outline form since we are assuming some previous introduction to the subject matter.

I. DEFINITIONS AND SIMPLE PROPERTIES

Let R be a nonempty set on which there are defined two binary operations called *addition* and *multiplication* and for which we use the familiar notation. Then R is a *ring* (with respect to the given addition and multiplication) provided the following properties (or laws) hold, it being understood that a, b, and c are arbitrary elements, distinct or identical, of R:

$$a + b = b + a \qquad \text{(\textit{commutative law of addition}).}$$

$$(a + b) + c = a + (b + c) \qquad \text{(\textit{associative law of addition}).}$$

There exists a zero element 0 of R such that for each $a \in R$

$$a + 0 = a \qquad \text{(\textit{existence of a zero}).}$$

If $a \in R$, there exists $x \in R$ such that

$$a + x = 0 \qquad \text{(\textit{existence of additive inverses}).}$$

$$(ab)c = a(bc) \qquad (associative\ law\ of\ multiplication).$$
$$a(b + c) = ab + ac,\ (b + c)a = ba + ca \qquad (distributive\ laws).$$

The first four of these defining properties of a ring are just the defining properties of an abelian group under (or with respect to) the operation of addition. This abelian group may be called the *additive group of the ring R*. Familiar properties of groups (or of rings) show that the zero of a ring is unique and that each element a of R has a unique additive inverse $-a$. We write $b + (-a)$ in the usual form $b - a$. Moreover, if c, $d \in R$, the equation $c + x = d$ has the unique solution $x = d - c$.

There exists a ring having only one element 0 with $0 + 0 = 0$ and $0 \cdot 0 = 0$. Of course, not much can be said about such a ring. Accordingly, we shall usually be interested in rings having more than one element and therefore having at least one nonzero element. We shall sometimes refer to a ring with more than one element as a *nonzero* ring.

A nonempty subset S of a ring R is naturally called a *subring* of R if S is itself a ring with respect to the operations of addition and multiplication in R. Every ring has two trivial subrings, R itself and the subring consisting of the zero element only. The following result, whose proof we leave to the reader, is frequently useful: *A nonempty subset S of a ring R is a subring of R if for all a, b ∈ S it is true that ab ∈ S and a − b ∈ S.*

The ring R is a *commutative ring* if $ab = ba$ for all elements a, b of R; otherwise it is a *noncommutative ring*.

1.1 Definition.   If there exists an element e_1 of the ring R such that $e_1 a = a$ for every element a of R, e_1 is called a *left unity of R*. If there exists an element e_2 of R such that $ae_2 = a$ for every element a of R, e_2 is called a *right unity* of R. If there exists an element e which is both a left unity and a right unity of R, then e is called a *unity* of R.

Alternative terms for *unity*, often found in the literature, are *identity* and *unit element*.

It is easy to verify that if a ring R has a left unity e_1 and a right unity e_2, then $e_1 = e_2$ and R has a unity. For since e_1 is a left unity, we must have $e_1 e_2 = e_2$. Similarly, since e_2 is a right unity, $e_1 e_2 = e_1$. Hence $e_1 = e_2$ and we have the desired result. This calculation also shows that if a ring has a unity, it is unique. However, a ring may very well have more than one left (right) unity, in which case it therefore cannot have a right (left) unity. Furthermore, if a ring has a *unique* left (right) unity, it is in fact the unity. (See 1.13, Exercises 15, 16.)

For each element a of a ring R,

$$a \cdot 0 = 0 \cdot a = 0.$$

Also, if a, b, $c \in R$, then

$$a(-b) = (-a)b = -(ab).$$

It is customary to write simply $-ab$ in place of $-(ab)$. Using this notation, it is then true that

$$a(b - c) = ab - ac,$$

and

$$(b - c)a = ba - ca.$$

Since addition and multiplication are binary operations, sums and products of more than two elements must be defined recursively. For example, if k is a positive integer such that $a_1 + a_2 + \cdots + a_k$ is defined, we define

$$a_1 + a_2 + \cdots + a_{k+1} = (a_1 + a_2 + \cdots + a_k) + a_{k+1}.$$

It is then possible to prove generalized associative and distributive laws. The generalized associative law of addition may be stated as follows:

Let n be a positive integer. If r is a positive integer such that $1 \leq r < n$, *we have*

$$(a_1 + a_2 + \cdots + a_r) + (a_{r+1} + \cdots + a_n) = a_1 + a_2 + \cdots + a_n.$$

In view of this result, it is customary to write sums without use of parentheses since the way parentheses might be inserted is immaterial. Of course, similar results hold for products as well.

If $a \in R$ and m is a positive integer, a^m is defined in the usual way. Moreover, for all positive integers m and n we have the following:

1.2
$$a^m \cdot a^n = a^{m+n},$$
$$(a^m)^n = a^{mn}.$$

These are often referred to as *laws of exponents*. If R is a *commutative* ring, and a, $b \in R$, then

1.3
$$(ab)^m = a^m \cdot b^m$$

for each positive integer m. In general, this familiar law of exponents does not hold for noncommutative rings.

If $a \in R$ and m is a positive integer, we define

$$ma = a + a + \cdots + a \qquad (m \text{ summands}).$$

We also define $0a = 0$ and $(-m)a = -(ma)$, and observe that $(-m)a = m(-a)$. If, now, $a, b \in R$, and m and n are arbitrary integers, the following hold:

$$ma + na = (m + n)a,$$
$$m(na) = (mn)a,$$
$$m(a + b) = ma + mb,$$
$$m(ab) = (ma)b = a(mb),$$
$$(ma)(nb) = (mn)(ab).$$

If a and b are elements of a *commutative ring* R and n is a positive integer, the familiar binomial expansion of $(a + b)^n$ holds as in elementary algebra. That is, if for each positive integer $r < n$, we define the positive integer $C(n, r)$ by

$$C(n, r) = \frac{n!}{r!(n - r)!},$$

then

1.4 $(a + b)^n = a^n + C(n, 1)a^{n-1}b + C(n, 2)a^{n-2}b^2 + \cdots$
$$+ C(n, n - 1)ab^{n-1} + b^n.$$

We now proceed to give a number of important definitions.

1.5 Definition. If there exists a positive integer n such that $na = 0$ for every element a of the ring R, the smallest such positive integer is called the *characteristic* of R. If no such positive integer exists, R is said to have *characteristic zero*.

1.6 Definition. An element a of a ring R is said to be a *divisor of zero* if there exists a nonzero element b of R such that $ab = 0$ or a nonzero element c of R such that $ca = 0$.

1.7 Definition. An element a of a ring R is said to be *nilpotent* if there exists a positive integer n such that $a^n = 0$.

It is trivial that the zero of a ring is nilpotent. Moreover, every nilpotent element is necessarily a divisor of zero. For if $a \neq 0$ and n is the smallest positive integer such that $a^n = 0$, then $n > 1$ and $a(a^{n-1}) = 0$ with $a^{n-1} \neq 0$.

1.8 Definition. A commutative ring (having more than one element) with unity and with no nonzero divisors of zero is said to be an *integral domain.*

It is a well-known fact that the characteristic of an integral domain is either zero or a prime.

1.9 Definition. Let R be a ring with unity 1, and let $a \in R$. If $a_1 \in R$ is such that $aa_1 = 1$, then a_1 is called a *right inverse* of a. If $a_2 \in R$ is such that $a_2a = 1$, then a_2 is called a *left inverse* of a. If $a' \in R$ is such that $aa' = a'a = 1$, then a' is called an *inverse* of a. An element which has an inverse is sometimes said to be a *unit* (not to be confused with the unity).

If $aa_1 = 1$ and $a_2a = 1$, then

$$a_1 = (a_2a)a_1 = a_2(aa_1) = a_2.$$

It follows that if an element a has both a right inverse and a left inverse, they are equal and a therefore has an inverse. Moreover, the above calculation also shows that if a has an inverse, it is unique. The unique inverse of a, if it exists, is usually denoted by a^{-1}. Clearly, the inverse of a^{-1} is a.

If a and b have inverses, then ab has an inverse as follows: $(ab)^{-1} = b^{-1}a^{-1}$. Hence, the set of all units of a ring R with unity is closed under the operation of multiplication.

If a has an inverse and we define $a^0 = 1$, $a^{-m} = (a^{-1})^m$ for $m > 0$, the laws of exponents 1.2 hold for *all* integers m and n.

1.10 Definition. An element e of a ring R is said to be *idempotent* if $e^2 = e$.

It is obvious that the zero is an idempotent element of every ring. Moreover, a left unity or right unity (in particular, a unity) is idempotent. However, there may very well exist many other idempotents. Examples will appear from time to time in these notes.

1.11 Definition. A nonzero ring with unity is called a *division ring* (or *skew field*) if every nonzero element has an inverse. A commutative division ring is called a *field*.

The reader is no doubt already familiar with the concept of field and has several examples in mind. However, the more general concept of division ring plays a central role in advanced algebraic theories. We might emphasize that a division ring may, but need not, be commutative. Later on we shall give some examples of division rings which are not fields, that is, of noncommutative division rings.

If a is a nonzero element and b an arbitrary element of a division ring D, it is clear that the equation $ax = b$ has the unique solution $x = a^{-1}b$ in D and the equation $ya = b$ has the unique solution $y = ba^{-1}$ in D.

It is well known that any integral domain can be imbedded in a field in essentially the same way that the field of rational numbers is usually constructed from the integral domain of integers. However, the commutativity of multiplication is essential in this construction.

1.12 Definition. A one-one mapping $a \to a'$ of a ring R onto a ring S is said to be an *isomorphism of R onto S* if the operations of addition and multiplication are preserved under this mapping, that is, if for a, $b \in R$, we have

$$(a + b)' = a' + b' \quad \text{and} \quad (ab)' = a'b'.$$

If there exists an isomorphism of R onto S, we say that *R is isomorphic to S* or that S is an *isomorphic image* of R, and indicate this fact by writing $R \cong S$.

An isomorphism of R onto a subring of S may be called an isomorphism of R *into* S, and if there exists such an isomorphism we may also say that S contains an isomorphic image of R.

It is clear that if $R \cong S$, then also $S \cong R$, and we may simply say that these two rings are isomorphic. In fact, if we have given a set of rings, the relation "isomorphic to" is an equivalence relation on the given set.

We conclude this section by presenting a few matters of notation and briefly mentioning some examples of rings with which the reader is no doubt familiar. Other examples will be introduced in later sections.

The ring of integers will be denoted by I, and $I/(n)$ will denote the ring of integers modulo n.

If R is an arbitrary ring and x an indeterminate, $R[x]$ will refer to the ring of all polynomials in x over R (that is, with coefficients in R). For simplicity, the construction of polynomial rings is sometimes carried out under the assumption that the coefficient ring is a commutative ring with unity. However, these are not essential restrictions, and we shall here let the ring of coefficients be completely arbitrary. The ring of polynomials in two indeterminates x and y with coefficients in a ring R may be denoted by $R[x, y]$, and so on.

It is an important fact that a polynomial ring $R[x]$ is an integral domain if and only if R is an integral domain. In particular, $R[x]$ is an integral domain if R is a field.

Let S be the set of all subsets of a given nonempty set A, including the empty set $\varnothing$ and the entire set A. If $a, b \in S$, we define ab to be $a \cap b$, the intersection of a and b. Also, $a + b$ is defined to be the set of all elements that are in subset a or in subset b but not in both (that is, $a + b$ consists of the elements in the union $a \cup b$ but not in the intersection $a \cap b$ of a and b). With respect to these definitions of addition and multiplication, S is a commutative ring with unity. It will be called the *ring of all subsets of A*. Note that every element of such a ring is idempotent.

Rings of matrices will be discussed a little later, but we here recall a special case which will be needed in the first list of exercises below. Let R be an arbitrary ring, and let us denote by R_2 the set of all matrices of order two over R, that is, the set of all matrices of the form

$$\begin{bmatrix} a & b \\ c & d \end{bmatrix},$$

where a, b, c, and d are elements of R. Then R_2 is a ring if we define addition and multiplication as follows:

$$\begin{bmatrix} a & b \\ c & d \end{bmatrix} + \begin{bmatrix} e & f \\ g & h \end{bmatrix} = \begin{bmatrix} a + e & b + f \\ c + g & d + h \end{bmatrix},$$

$$\begin{bmatrix} a & b \\ c & d \end{bmatrix} \cdot \begin{bmatrix} e & f \\ g & h \end{bmatrix} = \begin{bmatrix} ae + bg & af + bh \\ ce + dg & cf + dh \end{bmatrix}.$$

We shall naturally refer to R_2 as the *ring of all matrices of order two over R*.

2. IMBEDDING IN A RING WITH UNITY

It is an important fact that a ring without a unity can always be considered to be a subring of a ring with unity. Let R be an arbitrary ring, and let S be the set of all ordered pairs (a, i), where $a \in R$ and $i \in I$. On S we define addition and multiplication as follows:

$$(a, i) + (b, j) = (a + b, i + j),$$
$$(a, i)(b, j) = (ab + ib + ja, ij).$$

Then straightforward calculations will show that S is a ring with unity $(0, 1)$. Moreover, the set S' of all elements of S of the form $(a, 0)$, $a \in R$, is a subring of S which is isomorphic to R under the one-one mapping $(a, 0) \to a$. If we identify the elements of S' with the corresponding elements of R, we may consider R itself to be a subring of S.

Although the above construction is valid for an arbitrary ring R, it is of no importance if R has a unity. If R does have a unity to start with, it differs from the unity of S. Details of this imbedding process will be found in many books on abstract algebra.

1.13 EXERCISES

1. An element a of a ring R is said to *commute* with an element b of R if $ab = ba$. Show each of the following:
  (i) The set of those elements of R which commute with a fixed element a of R is a subring of R.
  (ii) The set of those elements of R which commute with every element of R is a subring of R. (This subring is called the *center* of R.)

2. Show that the set of all units in a ring with unity is a group with respect to the operation of multiplication.

3. Show that a ring R is a commutative ring if and only if for all elements a, b of R,

$$(a + b)^2 = a^2 + 2ab + b^2.$$

4. Prove each of the following:
  (i) If a ring with unity has more than one element, the zero and the unity are distinct.
  (ii) A nonzero idempotent in a ring cannot be nilpotent.
  (iii) An element of a ring (with unity) which has an inverse cannot be a divisor of zero.
  (iv) In a ring with unity and no nonzero divisors of zero the only idempotents are the zero and the unity.

5. Determine the number of nilpotent elements of each of the following rings: $I/(4)$, $I/(7)$, $I/(20)$, $I/(1000)$.

6. For what positive integers n does the ring $I/(n)$ have no nonzero nilpotent elements?

7. Find as many subrings as you can of the polynomial ring $K[x]$, where K is the field of real numbers.

8. If S is the ring of all subsets of an infinite set A, verify that the set T of all finite subsets of A is a subring of S. Show each of the following: **(i)** T does not have a unity; **(ii)** Every element of T is a divisor of zero in T; **(iii)** Every element of S except the unity is a divisor of zero in S.

9. If a and b are nilpotent elements of a commutative ring, show that $a + b$ is nilpotent.

10. Show that the word "commutative" is essential in the preceding exercise by exhibiting two nilpotent elements of the ring I_2 of all matrices of order two over I whose sum is not nilpotent.

11. Find all idempotent elements of each of the following rings: $I/(6)$, $I/(12)$, $I/(30)$.

12. If m and n are relatively prime integers greater than one, show that the ring $I/(mn)$ contains at least two idempotent elements other than the zero and the unity.

13. For what positive integers n does the ring $I/(n)$ have no idempotents other than the zero and the unity?

14. Prove that the two following conditions are equivalent for an arbitrary ring R:

(i) R has no nonzero nilpotent elements.

(ii) If $a \in R$ such that $a^2 = 0$, then $a = 0$.

15. Verify that the set S of all elements of I_2 of the form

$$\begin{bmatrix} a & b \\ 0 & 0 \end{bmatrix}, \qquad\qquad a, b \in I,$$

is a subring of I_2. Then show each of the following:

(i) S has a left unity but no right unity.

(ii) S has an infinite number of distinct left unities.

16. Prove that if a ring has a unique left unity, it is also a right unity (and therefore a unity).

17. Find as many subrings as you can of the ring K_2 of all matrices of order two over the field K of real numbers.

18. Prove that if a and b are elements of a commutative ring with unity such that a has an inverse and b is nilpotent, then $a + b$ has an inverse.

19. By an example using matrices of order two show that the word "commutative" is essential in the statement of the preceding exercise.

20. Find the inverse of the element $2x^2 + 2x + 3$ in the polynomial ring $I/(4)[x]$. Do the same for the element $4x^3 + 6x^2 + 2x + 5$ in the polynomial ring $I/(8)[x]$.

21. If S is the set of all elements of the ring I_2 (of all matrices of order two over the ring I of integers) of the form

$$\begin{bmatrix} n & 0 \\ 2n & 0 \end{bmatrix}, \qquad\qquad n \in I,$$

verify that S is an isomorphic image of the ring I. Find several other sub-rings of I_2 that are isomorphic images of I.

22. A ring is called a *Boolean ring* if it has more than one element and all of its elements are idempotent. Prove each of the following:

(i) A Boolean ring has characteristic 2.

(ii) A Boolean ring is necessarily commutative.

(iii) Every element of a Boolean ring except the unity (if it has one) is a divisor of zero.

23. If the ring R has no nonzero nilpotent elements, any idempotent e of R commutes with all elements of R (that is, $ex = xe$ for every $x \in R$).

24. Show that if R has no nonzero nilpotent elements, the ring S with unity as constructed in Section 2 has no nonzero nilpotent elements.

25. Suppose that R is a ring with positive characteristic n, and let S be the set of all ordered pairs (a, i^*), $a \in R$, $i^* \in I/(n)$. If on S addition and multiplication are defined by

$$(a, i^*) + (b, j^*) = (a + b, i^* + j^*),$$

and

$$(a, i^*)(b, j^*) = (ab + ib + ja, i^*j^*),$$

show that multiplication is well-defined, that S is a ring with unity which contains a subring isomorphic to R, and that S also has characteristic n.

26. If R is a ring with more than one element and with the property that for each nonzero element a there exists a *unique* element b of R such that $aba = a$, prove in turn each of the following:

(i) R has no nonzero divisors of zero.

(ii) $bab = b$.

(iii) R has a unity.

(iv) R is a division ring.

3. ALGEBRAS

Some important classes of rings are called *algebras*. Let us recall the definition as follows.

1.14. Definition. Let A be a nonempty set on which there are defined binary operations of addition and multiplication and also a scalar multiplication by elements of a field F. Then A is *an algebra over the field F* if the following conditions are satisfied:

(i) A is a vector space over F with respect to the operations of addition and scalar multiplication.

(ii) A is a ring with respect to the operations of addition and multiplication.

(iii) If u, $v \in A$ and $a \in F$, then $(au)v = u(av) = a(uv)$.

If F' is a *field* which contains the field F, then in a natural way F' may be considered to be an algebra over F. For we already have operations of addition and multiplication in F'; and if $a \in F$ and $a' \in F'$, we also define scalar multiplication aa' to be multiplication in the field F'. As a simple example, the field C of complex numbers is an algebra over the field K of real numbers. As a vector space over K, clearly C is of dimension two since $\{1, i\}$ is a basis.

Another example with which the reader is no doubt familiar is the algebra F_n of all matrices of order n over a field F. An element of F_n is of the form

$$
1.15 \qquad \begin{bmatrix} a_{11} & a_{12} & \cdots & a_{1n} \\ a_{21} & a_{22} & \cdots & a_{2n} \\ \cdot & \cdot & \cdots & \cdot \\ a_{n1} & a_{n2} & \cdots & a_{nn} \end{bmatrix},
$$

where all $a_{ij} \in F$. If the order of such a matrix is understood (for example, if it is known that it is an element of F_n), it is customary to designate the above matrix by (a_{ij}). Using this notation, addition, multiplication, and scalar multiplication in F_n are defined as follows:

$$
(a_{ij}) + (b_{ij}) = (a_{ij} + b_{ij}),
$$

$$
1.16 \qquad (a_{ij})(b_{ij}) = \left(\sum_{k=1}^{n} a_{ik} b_{kj} \right),
$$

$$
c(a_{ij}) = (ca_{ij}), \qquad\qquad\qquad c \in F.
$$

We shall return to this example a little later, but let us next make some general observations about algebras. Accordingly, let A be an algebra over a field F. We shall here assume that, as a vector space over F, A has finite dimension n. Let $\{X_1, X_2, \ldots, X_n\}$ be a basis of A as a vector space over F, so that each element of A is uniquely expressible as a linear combination of these basis elements. In particular, since we have a multiplication defined on A, any product of basis elements is such a linear combination. That is, there exist uniquely determined elements c_{ijk} of F such that

$$
1.17 \qquad\qquad X_i X_j = \sum_{k=1}^{n} c_{ijk} X_k, \qquad\qquad i, j = 1, 2, \ldots, n.
$$

Moreover, every product of elements of A can be calculated by making use of equations 1.17. To see this, let $\sum_{i=1}^{n} a_i X_i$ and $\sum_{j=1}^{n} b_j X_j$ be elements of A. Then using 1.17, and the other properties of an algebra, we have

1.18
$$\left(\sum_{i=1}^{n} a_i X_i \right)\left(\sum_{j=1}^{n} b_j X_j \right) = \sum_{i, j=1}^{n} a_i b_j X_i X_j$$
$$= \sum_{i, j, k=1}^{n} a_i b_j c_{ijk} X_k.$$

In the preceding remarks we started with an algebra A over F. However, a somewhat different viewpoint is much more important. Suppose that we merely start with a vector space A over F, and let $\{X_1, X_2, \ldots, X_n\}$ be a basis of this vector space. Now suppose that $c_{ijk}(i, j, k = 1, 2, \ldots, n)$ are elements of F and let us *define* multiplication of these basis elements by 1.17, and then proceed to *define* multiplication of arbitrary elements of A by 1.18. If we do this, it is easy to verify that all but one of the properties of an algebra will be satisfied. The one exception is that multiplication need not be associative, and hence A may lack this ring property. However, *if* the c_{ijk} are so chosen that multiplication of the basis elements is associative, it can be shown that multiplication of arbitrary elements is associative and we will have an algebra. Examples of algebras are most easily given by this method, that is, by specifying the multiplication formulas (1.17) for the basis elements. Of course, it is possible to determine general conditions on the multiplication constants c_{ijk} so that multiplication will be associative, but these are too complicated to be of much practical use in constructing examples of algebras.

One very easy way to construct algebras by the method just presented is to start with a finite *group* G with operation multiplication. Suppose that G is of order n and that the elements of G are g_i $(i = 1, 2, \ldots, n)$. Now take a vector space V of dimension n over an arbitrary field F. By a proper choice of notation, we may let $\{X_{g_1}, X_{g_2}, \ldots, X_{g_n}\}$ be a basis of V over F. We make use of the given multiplication in G to define multiplication of these basis elements as follows:

1.19
$$X_{g_i} X_{g_j} = X_{g_i g_j} \qquad i, j = 1, 2, \ldots, n.$$

This is the form that equations 1.17 take in this special case. If we now define multiplication of arbitrary elements of V as in 1.18, we know that this multiplication is associative since multiplication is associative in G. The algebra that we get by this method is called the *group algebra of the group G over the field F*.

As another illustration, let us again consider the field C of complex numbers. However, this time we start by considering it to be merely a vector space with basis $\{1, i\}$ over the field K of real numbers, and we then define (1.17) multiplication of these basis elements as follows:

1.20 $\qquad 1 \cdot 1 = 1, \quad 1 \cdot i = i, \quad i \cdot 1 = i, \quad i \cdot i = -1.$

If we extend this definition of multiplication to arbitrary elements of C, as in 1.18, we obtain the algebra of complex numbers over the reals. Since 1 is the unity of C, we might naturally omit the first three equations of 1.20 and consider that the multiplication is defined by the single equation $i^2 = -1$.

We now use this same general approach to give another example of more interest. Let Q be a vector space of dimension four over the field K of real numbers, and let us denote a basis of Q by $\{1, i, j, k\}$. We shall make Q into an algebra over K by suitable definition of multiplication of these basis elements. The element 1 is to be the unity of Q, so we need not explicitly define the products of 1 with the other basis elements. The remaining products (1.17) are specified as follows:

$$i^2 = -1, \quad j^2 = -1, \quad k^2 = -1, \quad ij = k, \quad ji = -k,$$
$$jk = i, \quad kj = -i, \quad ki = j, \quad ik = -j.$$

A simple way to exhibit these products is by the following multiplication table.

		i	j	k
	i	-1	k	$-j$
1.21	j	$-k$	-1	i
	k	j	$-i$	-1

It is to be understood that the product of any element in the left column by any element in the top row (in this order) is to be found at the intersection of the respective row and column.

The elements of Q are of the form $a + bi + cj + dk$, where a, b, c, d are real numbers. It may be verified that multiplication of elements of Q is associative, and therefore that Q is an algebra over K. It is clearly a noncommutative algebra. If $q \in Q$ with $q = a + bi + cj + dk$, the element q^* of Q defined by $q^* = a - bi - cj - dk$ is called the *conjugate* of Q. A simple calculation will show that

1.22 $\qquad qq^* = q^*q = a^2 + b^2 + c^2 + d^2.$

If $q \neq 0$, not all of a, b, c, and d can be zero and hence qq^* is a nonzero *real number*. It follows from 1.22 that if $q \neq 0$, then q has an inverse $(qq^*)^{-1}q^*$ in Q. Hence Q is a division ring. This division ring is called the algebra (or ring) of *real quaternions*. This algebra, as well as the name, was introduced by Hamilton a little over a century ago.

Let us return to a brief consideration of the algebra F_n of all matrices of order n over a field F. For each $i, j = 1, 2, \ldots, n$, we define E_{ij} to be the matrix with 1 at the intersection of the ith row and j^{th} column and zeros elsewhere. Then these n^2 matrices E_{ij} $(i, j = 1, 2, \ldots, n)$, which are often called *matrix units*, form a basis of F_n over F since an element 1.15 of F_n is uniquely expressible in the form

$$1.23 \qquad \sum_{i, j = 1}^{n} a_{ij} E_{ij}.$$

If the definition of the product of two matrices is applied to a product of these basis elements, we obtain the following formulas:

$$1.24 \qquad E_{pq} E_{rs} = \begin{cases} E_{ps} & \text{if } q = r, \\ 0 & \text{if } q \neq r. \end{cases}$$

This is the form that equations 1.17 take in this particular case. In calculations with matrices it is often convenient to express the matrices in the form 1.23 and to make use of formulas 1.24 in computing products. It may be observed that the matrix units of the form E_{kk} are idempotent.

There is an important generalization of the algebra F_n as follows. Let R be a completely arbitrary ring, and consider matrices of the form 1.15 where now the a_{ij} are elements of R. If we define addition and multiplication of such matrices by the first two of equations 1.16, we get a ring which will be denoted by R_n and called *the ring of all matrices of order n over R*. We shall also refer to this ring as *the complete matrix ring R_n*. Multiplication of elements of R by elements of R_n may naturally be defined by the third of equations 1.16. If R has a unity 1, the matrix units E_{ij} are now elements of R_n. Moreover, if $r \in R$, rE_{ij} is the element of R_n with r at the intersection of the ith row and j^{th} column and zeros elsewhere, and each element of R_n is uniquely expressible in the form 1.23 just as in the case in which R is a field. If $a, b \in R$, it is easy to verify that

$$(aE_{pq})(bE_{rs}) = \begin{cases} (ab)E_{ps} & \text{if } q = r, \\ 0 & \text{if } q \neq r. \end{cases}$$

Thus, although we are not now working in an algebra, the product of two elements of R_n, given in the form 1.23, can be computed by use of formulas 1.24 essentially as in the case of an algebra. We shall make use of this convenient fact from time to time in the sequel.

The matrix $E = E_{11} + E_{22} + \cdots + E_{nn}$, which has 1's along the principal diagonal and zeros elsewhere, is the unity of R_n. A matrix of the form aE, where $a \in R$, is often called a *scalar matrix*.

4. FORMAL POWER SERIES

Let R be a ring and x an indeterminate, and let $R[[x]]$ denote the set of all expressions of the form

1.25
$$f = \sum_{k=0}^{\infty} a_k x^k, \qquad a_k \in R; k = 0, 1, 2, \ldots .$$

If

1.26
$$g = \sum_{k=0}^{\infty} b_k x^k$$

is also an element of $R[[x]]$, we define addition and multiplication in $R[[x]]$ as follows:

1.27
$$f + g = \sum_{k=0}^{\infty} (a_k + b_k) x^k,$$

and

1.28
$$fg = \sum_{k=0}^{\infty} d_k x^k,$$

where

$$d_k = \sum_{i+j=k} a_i b_j, \qquad k = 0, 1, 2, \ldots .$$

Then it may be verified that $R[[x]]$ is a ring which is called the *ring of formal power series* (in the indeterminate x) *over* R. It is to be understood, of course, that $f = g$ means that $a_k = b_k$ for all nonnegative integers k.

If we agree, as in working with polynomials, that coefficients not indicated are understood to be zero, the elements of R themselves may be considered to be elements of $R[[x]]$. That is, $R[[x]]$ contains the ring R as a subring. In particular, if R has a unity 1, it is also the unity of $R[[x]]$. Moreover, for example, if n is a positive integer, we may consider x^n to be an element of $R[[x]]$. Of course, we interpret it to be the formal power series with x^n having coefficient 1 and all other coefficients being zero.

We shall next prove the following result.

1.29   Lemma.   *Suppose that R has a unity 1. The element f of $R[[x]]$, given by 1.25, has an inverse in $R[[x]]$ if and only if a_0 has an inverse in R.*

Proof: One part of this is almost trivial. For if g, given by 1.26, is such that $fg = gf = 1$, Definition 1.28 of multiplication shows that $a_0 b_0 = b_0 a_0 = 1$, and b_0 is the inverse of a_0.

Conversely, suppose that a_0 has an inverse in R and let us show that there exists an element g of $R[[x]]$ which is the inverse of f. We tentatively consider g to be of the form 1.26 and show that it is possible to determine the coefficients b_k of g in such a way that $g = f^{-1}$. To start with, we shall determine the coefficients b_k so that $fg = 1$, that is, so that g is a *right inverse* of f. From $fg = 1$, we obtain from Definition 1.28 the following equations which, if satisfied by the coefficients of g, will imply that g is a right inverse of f:

1.30
$$
\begin{aligned}
a_0 b_0 &= 1, \\
a_0 b_1 + a_1 b_0 &= 0, \\
a_0 b_2 + a_1 b_1 + a_2 b_0 &= 0, \\
\cdot \quad \cdot \quad \cdot & \quad \cdot \quad \cdot \quad \cdot \quad \cdot \\
a_0 b_n + a_1 b_{n-1} + \cdots + a_n b_0 &= 0, \\
a_0 b_{n+1} + a_1 b_n + \cdots + a_n b_1 + a_{n+1} b_0 &= 0, \\
\cdot \quad \cdot \quad \cdot \quad \cdot & \quad \cdot \quad \cdot \quad \cdot \quad \cdot \quad \cdot
\end{aligned}
$$

Now, since it is given that a_0 has an inverse, the first of these equations determines b_0 uniquely as a_0^{-1}. Then b_1 is determined from the second of these equations as follows:

$$ b_1 = -a_0^{-1} a_1 b_0. $$

By induction, if $b_0, b_1, \ldots, b_n$ have been determined, b_{n+1} is determined by the last displayed equation in 1.30. Accordingly, every b_k is determined by the equation $fg = 1$, and f has a right inverse g. By a similar calculation, it can be shown that f has a left inverse. However, in any ring an element with a right inverse and a left inverse has an inverse, and the lemma is established.

We shall use this lemma a little later. However, we first introduce a new ring which will contain the ring $R[[x]]$ as a subring. To this end, we consider the set $R\langle x \rangle$ of all expressions of the form

$$\sum_{k=-\infty}^{\infty} a_k x^k, \qquad \text{all } a_k \in R,$$

with the understanding that at most a finite number of the coefficients a_k with k a *negative* integer are different from zero. If addition and multiplication of elements of $R\langle x \rangle$ are defined precisely as in 1.27 and 1.28 (except that now k may also be a negative integer) we make $R\langle x \rangle$ into a ring which clearly contains the ring $R[[x]]$. We may call $R\langle x \rangle$ the ring of *extended formal power series over R*. At any rate, our different notation should always make it clear which ring we are referring to. We shall now prove the following theorem.

1.31   **Theorem.**   *If R is a division ring, the ring $R\langle x \rangle$ also is a division ring.*

Proof: Let $f = \sum_{k=-\infty}^{\infty} a_k x^k$ be a nonzero element of $R\langle x \rangle$, and suppose that r is the uniquely determined integer such that $a_r \neq 0$ and $a_s = 0$ for every integer $s < r$. Then $x^{-r}f$ is an element of $R[[x]]$ which has an inverse h in $R[[x]]$ by Lemma 1.29. It follows that $x^{-r}h$ is the inverse of f in $R\langle x \rangle$, and the proof is completed.

It is obvious that the ring $R\langle x \rangle$ is commutative if and only if R is commutative. As a consequence of the preceding theorem, we therefore have at hand another example of a noncommutative division ring, namely, the ring $Q\langle x \rangle$ of extended formal power series over the division ring of real quaternions.

5. DIRECT SUMS

In this section we shall briefly introduce some concepts which will be discussed in more detail, and with greater generality, in Chapter 3.

We start with a finite number n of rings S_i $(i = 1, 2, \ldots, n)$, and construct from them a new ring as follows. Let S be the product set $S_1 \times S_2 \times \cdots \times S_n$, that is, the set of all ordered n-tuples

$$(a_1, a_2, \ldots, a_n), \qquad a_i \in S_i; \, i = 1, 2, \ldots, n.$$

We define operations of addition and multiplication on S in the following natural way:

1.32 $(a_1, a_2, \ldots, a_n) + (b_1, b_2, \ldots, b_n) =$
$$(a_1 + b_1, a_2 + b_2, \ldots, a_n + b_n),$$

and

1.33 $(a_1, a_2, \ldots, a_n)(b_1, b_2, \ldots, b_n) = (a_1 b_1, a_2 b_2, \ldots, a_n b_n).$

It is then easy to verify that S is a ring. This ring is called the *direct sum of the rings S_i* $(i = 1, 2, \ldots, n)$ and often designated by $S_1 \oplus S_2 \oplus \cdots \oplus S_n$. The rings S_i may be called the *component rings* of this direct sum. More precisely, S_i is the ith component $(i = 1, 2, \ldots, n)$. Moreover, if $(a_1, a_2, \ldots, a_n) \in S$, it is convenient to call a_i the ith *component* of this element and to refer to addition and multiplication in S (defined by 1.32 and 1.33) as *componentwise* addition and multiplication.

The zero of S is the element whose i^{th} component is the zero of S_i for all $i = 1, 2, \ldots, n$. Clearly, S has a unity if and only if every S_i has a unity, and if S has a unity an element of S has an inverse if and only if for each i its ith component has an inverse in S_i.

The set U_1 of all elements of S of the form $(a_1, 0, \ldots, 0)$, $a_1 \in S_1$, is a subring of S. Moreover, the mapping $a_1 \to (a_1, 0, \ldots, 0)$ clearly defines an isomorphism of S_1 onto U_1. Hence S contains an isomorphic image U_1 of S_1. Of course, in like manner, S contains an isomorphic image U_i of each component ring S_i $(i = 1, 2, \ldots, n)$.

In the direct sum S defined above, the component rings appeared in the particular *order $S_1, S_2, \ldots, S_n$*. However, it is easy to verify that any other order would give a direct sum isomorphic to S (see 1.35, Exercise 12). Accordingly, whenever it is convenient to do so, we shall not hesitate to speak of the direct sum of a *set* (not necessarily ordered) of rings.

Later on, we shall extend and generalize the concept of direct sum in various ways. However, we may point out here one simple extension as follows. Suppose that instead of a finite number we have a denumerably infinite number of rings S_i $(i = 1, 2, 3, \ldots)$. In this case, we shall see that there are two different concepts, either of which might be considered a natural generalization of the direct sum of a finite number of rings. The set S of *all* infinite sequences

1.34 $(a_1, a_2, a_3, \ldots),$ $a_i \in S_i; i = 1, 2, 3, \ldots,$

with componentwise addition and multiplication is a ring, which we shall call the *complete direct sum* of the rings S_i $(i = 1, 2, 3, \ldots)$. As in the finite case, S contains an isomorphic image U_i of each component ring S_i. In the present situation, there is another subring of S of some interest. Let T be the subring of S consisting of all elements 1.34 with the property that at most a finite number of the components a_i are different from zero. This ring T is called the *discrete direct sum* of the rings S_i $(i = 1, 2, 3, \ldots)$. Note that T contains each of the subrings U_i defined above. Both S and T generalize the concept of direct sum of a finite number of rings.

1.35 EXERCISES

1. The algebra of quaternions over an arbitrary field F has elements of the form $a + bi + cj + dk$, where a, b, c, d are elements of F and multiplication of the basis elements is defined as in 1.21. Show each of the following:

(i) The algebra of quaternions over the field of rational numbers is a division ring.

(ii) The algebra of quaternions over the field of complex numbers is not a division ring. (You must use a notation which will distinguish between the complex number $\sqrt{-1}$ and the basis element i of quaternions.)

(iii) The algebra of quaternions over the field $I/(2)$ is not a division ring.

2. In the algebra Q of real quaternions show that there are an infinite number of elements X such that $X^2 + 1 = 0$.

3. Let R be an arbitrary ring and m and n positive integers. Then by $(R_m)_n$ we naturally mean the ring of all matrices of order n whose elements are matrices of order m over R. It is true that always $(R_m)_n \cong R_{mn}$. Write out a careful proof of this fact for the case in which $m = n = 2$.

4. Let G be a cyclic group of order three, and F an arbitrary field. Show that the group algebra of G over the field F has nonzero divisors of zero.

5. If C is the field of complex numbers and Q the division ring of real quaternions, verify that the mapping

$$a + bi + cj + dk \rightarrow \begin{bmatrix} a + bi & c + di \\ -c + di & a - bi \end{bmatrix}$$

is an isomorphism of Q onto a subring of C_2. How can you use this fact to establish (without calculation) the associative law of multiplication for real quaternions?

6. If q is a real quaternion, the real number qq^* is called the *norm* of q and denoted by $N(q)$. Show that $N(q_1 q_2) = N(q_1)N(q_2)$.

7. Determine the center (defined in 1.13, Exercise 1) of the ring Q of real quaternions.

8. If R is a commutative ring with unity and n is a positive integer, show that the center of the matrix ring R_n consists of all scalar matrices of R_n.

9. If R is a ring with unity, x an indeterminate, and n a positive integer, show each of the following:

(i) $R_n[x] \cong (R[x])_n$.

(ii) $R_n[[x]] \cong (R[[x]])_n$.

10. In the field $K\langle x \rangle$ of extended formal power series over the field K of real numbers, determine the inverse of each of the following: (i) x^{10},

(ii) $1 + x$, (iii) $\sum\limits_{k=0}^{\infty} 2^k x^k$, (iv) $\sum\limits_{k=-3}^{\infty} x^k$.

11. Exhibit an isomorphism of the ring $I/(6)$ onto the direct sum of the rings $I/(2)$ and $I/(3)$.

12. If S_i ($i = 1, 2, 3$) are arbitrary rings, verify that $S_1 \oplus S_2 \oplus S_3 \cong S_2 \oplus S_1 \oplus S_3$. Generalize this result.

13. Let S be the direct sum of rings S_i ($i = 1, 2, \ldots, n$), it being understood that $n \geq 2$ and that each ring S_i has more than one element. Show each of the following:

(i) S cannot be an integral domain.

(ii) An element of S is a divisor of zero if and only if at least one of its components is a divisor of zero.

(iii) An element of S is nilpotent if and only if all of its components are nilpotent.

14. Let T be the discrete direct sum of an infinite number of rings S_i ($i = 1, 2, 3, \ldots$). Show each of the following:

(i) Every element of T is a divisor of zero in T.

(ii) If n is a positive integer and $k_1, k_2, \ldots, k_n$ are any n positive integers, T contains a subring isomorphic to $S_{k_1} \oplus S_{k_2} \oplus \cdots \oplus S_{k_n}$.

(iii) T cannot have a unity (assuming that each ring S_i has more than one element).

15. Let R be a given ring (with more than one element) and let S be the complete direct sum of a denumerable number of rings each identical with R. Show that the mapping

$$(a_1, a_2, a_3, \ldots) \to (0, a_1, a_2, \ldots)$$

defines an isomorphism of S onto a subring of S.

16. Show that if R has a unity, a sum of distinct matric units of the form E_{kk} is an idempotent in the complete matrix ring R_n.

Ideals and Homomorphisms

IN THIS CHAPTER we introduce and briefly discuss some important concepts that play a central role in the theory of rings. Therefore, a mastery of the ideas presented in this chapter is essential to an understanding of much of the material to be found in later chapters.

6. IDEALS

Unless otherwise stated, R will denote an arbitrary ring which we shall usually tacitly assume has more than one element.

2.1 Definition. Let A be a nonempty subset of a ring R with the property that, with respect to the operation of addition, A is a subgroup of the additive group of R. Then

(i) A is a *right ideal* in R if it is closed under multiplication on the right by elements of R (that is, if $ar \in A$ for each $a \in A$ and $r \in R$).

(ii) A is a *left ideal* in R if it is closed under multiplication on the left by elements of R.

(iii) A is an *ideal* in R if it is both a right ideal in R and a left ideal in R.

If a and b are elements of a right ideal (or left ideal) A in R, then certainly $ab \in A$ so that A is itself closed under the operation of multiplication. It follows readily that every right ideal (or left ideal) in R is a subring of R. Moreover, a subring of R is a right ideal (left ideal) in R if and only if it is closed under multiplication on the right (left) by elements of R.

It may be instructive to give an example of a subring which is not a right ideal or a left ideal. Consider the set S of all elements of the complete matrix ring I_2 that are of the form

$$\begin{bmatrix} i & 0 \\ 0 & 0 \end{bmatrix}, \qquad i \in I.$$

It is easily verified that S is a subring of I_2. However, it is not true that S is closed under multiplication on either the right or the left by arbitrary elements of I_2, and hence S is neither a right ideal nor a left ideal in I_2.

If, in some context, it seems desirable to emphasize that we are considering an ideal and not merely a right ideal or a left ideal, we may occasionally refer to an ideal as a *two-sided* ideal.

For simplicity of statement, we shall concentrate on right ideals and seldom mention left ideals. However, it will usually be obvious that analogous results hold for left ideals.

It is clear that the concepts of right ideal and ideal coincide in a commutative ring. However, it is important to distinguish between them in noncommutative rings.

We observed in the preceding chapter that every ring R has two trivial subrings, the entire ring R and the zero subring (consisting of the zero element only). It is clear that these two subrings are in fact ideals in R; hence every ring has these two trivial or improper ideals. Any other ideal (right ideal) is sometimes called a *proper* ideal (right ideal).

We gave in Section 1 a useful criterion for determining whether a given set of elements of R is a subring of R. This may easily be extended as follows: *A nonempty set A of elements of a ring R is a right ideal in R if and only if for all a, $b \in A$ and every $r \in R$, $a - b \in A$ and $ar \in A$.* We leave the proof of this to the reader, and also the formulation of a corresponding result for ideals.

EXAMPLE 1. Let n be a fixed element of the ring I of integers, and let $N = \{ni \mid i \in I\}$. Then N is an ideal in I. It will be proved (2.8) that every ideal in I is of this form for some choice of the integer n.

EXAMPLE 2. In this example, we consider the ring K_2 of all matrices of order two over the field K of real numbers. Let U be the set of all elements of K_2 of the form

$$\begin{bmatrix} a & b \\ 0 & 0 \end{bmatrix}, \qquad\qquad a, b \in K;$$

let V be the set of all elements of K_2 of the form

$$\begin{bmatrix} a & 0 \\ b & 0 \end{bmatrix}, \qquad\qquad a, b \in K;$$

and let W be the set of all elements of K_2 of the form

$$\begin{bmatrix} a & b \\ 0 & c \end{bmatrix}, \qquad a, b, c \in K.$$

Then it may be verified that U is a right ideal (and not a left ideal) in K_2, that V is a left ideal (and not a right ideal) in K_2, and that W is a subring (neither a right ideal nor a left ideal) of K_2.

EXAMPLE 3.   Let S_i $(i = 1, 2, \ldots, n)$ be given rings and let $S = S_1 \oplus S_2 \oplus \cdots \oplus S_n$, the direct sum of these rings. It has already been observed in Section 5 of the preceding chapter that the set U_i of all elements of S having j^{th} components zero for all $j \neq i$ is a subring of S which is isomorphic to S_i $(i = 1, 2, \ldots, n)$. We now observe that these subrings U_i are in fact ideals in S. More generally, if for every $i = 1, 2, \ldots, n$, A_i is an ideal (right ideal) in S_i, then $A_1 \oplus A_2 \oplus \cdots \oplus A_n$ is an ideal (right ideal) in S. By considering the special case in which each A_i is a trivial ideal in S_i (that is, either the zero ideal or S_i), we see that the set of all elements of S which have any fixed set of components all equal to zero is an ideal in S.

It is easy to verify that the intersection of any set of ideals (right ideals) in a ring R is an ideal (right ideal) in R. If K is a set of elements of R, there always exists at least one ideal, R itself, which contains K. Accordingly, the intersection of all ideals (right ideals) in R which contain K is an ideal (right ideal) uniquely determined by K.

2.2 Definition.   The intersection of all ideals (right ideals) in a ring R which contain a given nonempty set K of elements of R is called the ideal (right ideal) *generated* by K.

The special case in which the set K consists of a single element a of R is of sufficient importance that we make the following additional definition.

2.3 Definition.   An ideal (right ideal) in R generated by one element of R is called a *principal* ideal (right ideal). The ideal (right ideal) generated by the element a is denoted by (a) (by $(a)_r$).

In this notation, (0) is clearly the zero ideal. Also, if R has a unity e, each ideal (right ideal) which contains e certainly contains $r = er$ for each $r \in R$. Hence $(e) = (e)_r = R$. More generally, if R has a unity and a is an element of R which has a right inverse b, then $(a)_r = R$ since for every element t of R we have $t = a(bt) \in (a)_r$. If R is a *division ring*, $(a)_r = R$ for every nonzero element a of R. It follows that a division ring R has *only* the two trivial ideals (0) and R.

Let us next consider in some detail the principal right ideal $(a)_r$, where $a \in R$. It is a right ideal which contains a, and it is therefore closed under subtraction (and addition) as well as under multiplication on the right by elements of R. Hence, $(a)_r$ must contain all elements of the set $\{na + at \mid n \in I, t \in R\}$. But it is readily verified that this set is itself closed under subtraction. Also, if $na + at$ is an element of this set and $u \in R$, then $(na + at)u = 0 \cdot a + a(nu + tu)$ is an element of this set. Hence, we also have closure under multiplication on the right by elements of R. It follows that this set is a right ideal containing a and hence containing $(a)_r$. We have therefore shown that

$$2.4 \qquad (a)_r = \{na + at \mid n \in I, t \in R\}.$$

It is customary to denote by aR the set $\{at \mid t \in R\}$. Now aR is itself a right ideal in R and† $aR \subseteq (a)_r$, but aR need not necessarily contain the element a. Hence we may very well have $aR \subset (a)_r$. However, if R has a unity e, certainly $a = ae \in aR$. Moreover, in this case, $na + at = a(ne + t) \in aR$. These observations establish the following result.

$$2.5 \qquad \textit{If } R \textit{ has a unity, then } (a)_r = aR = \{at \mid t \in R\}.$$

As an illustration of these concepts, let E be the ring of all even integers. It is easy to verify that $(4)_r$ (or simply (4) since E is commutative) consists of all the integers which are divisible by 4. However, $4E$ consists of all integers divisible by 8.

In 2.4 and 2.5 we have given explicit expressions for the elements of a principal right ideal. Corresponding expressions for principal ideals are somewhat more complicated but are sometimes useful. We now state these results and leave the proofs as exercises.

The principal ideal (a) generated by an element a of an arbitrary ring R is as follows:

$$2.6 \qquad (a) = \{na + sa + at + \sum s_i a t_i \mid n \in I \text{ and } s, t, s_i, t_i \in R\},$$

---

† We shall consistently write $C \subseteq D$ (or $D \supseteq C$) to indicate that C is a subset of D. If C is a subset of D and $C \neq D$, we shall write $C \subset D$ (or $D \supset C$).

it being understood that $\sum$ represents an arbitrary finite sum with one or more terms.

2.7   *If R has a unity, then $(a) = \{\sum s_i a t_i \mid s_i, t_i \in R\}$.*

Of course, if R is commutative, 2.6 reduces to 2.4, and 2.7 to 2.5. In the noncommutative case the complication arises from the fact that, for example, an expression such as $s_1 a t_1 + s_2 a t_2$ cannot be written as a single term and, accordingly, our expressions for (a) must include all finite sums of the form $\sum s_i a t_i$ since otherwise we would not have closure under addition.

The following theorem states that in certain commutative rings every ideal is principal.

2.8 Theorem. *In each of the commutative rings listed below every ideal is a principal ideal:*

(i) *The ring I of integers.*

(ii) *The ring $F[x]$ of polynomials in an indeterminate x over a field F.*

(iii) *The ring $F[[x]]$ of formal power series in an indeterminate x over a field F. In this ring, every nonzero ideal is of the form (x^k) for some nonnegative integer k.*

We shall prove the first part of this theorem and list the proofs of the other two parts as exercises below.

Suppose that A is an ideal in the ring I. If A is the zero ideal, then $A = (0)$ is the principal ideal generated by 0. If $A \neq (0)$, A contains positive integers, and let us assume that n is the smallest positive integer which is in the ideal A. Certainly, $(n) \subseteq A$ and we only need to prove that $A \subseteq (n)$. Let $a \in A$. By the division algorithm, there exist integers q and r such that :

$$a = qn + r, \qquad\qquad 0 \leq r < n.$$

Since $a \in A$, $n \in A$ and $r = (a - qn)$ it follows that $r \in A$. If $r > 0$, we have a contradiction to the assumption that n is the smallest positive integer in A. Accordingly, $r = 0$ and $a = qn$. It follows that $a \in (n)$, so $A \subseteq (n)$ and the proof is completed.

There are many rings in which there exist ideals that are not principal ideals. As one simple example, in the polynomial ring $I[x]$ with coefficients that are integers, let B be the set of all polynomials with *even* constant terms. It is easy to verify that B is an ideal in $I[x]$. If B were a principal ideal, by 2.5 all elements of B would have to be multiples of some one polynomial. Since this is not true, B cannot be a principal ideal.

2.9   EXERCISES

1. Show that if A and B are ideals (right ideals) in a ring R and $A \subseteq B$, then A is an ideal (right ideal) in the ring B.

2. Make use of the matrix units E_{ij} (as in 1.23 and 1.24) to prove the statements made about the sets U, V, and W in Example 2.

3. Prove that the set U of Example 2 is the principal right ideal $(E_{11})_r$.

4. Show that the set of all nilpotent elements of a commutative ring R is an ideal in R (cf. 1.13, Exercise 9).

5. Let A be an ideal in the commutative ring R, and let A' be the set of all elements r of R such that $r^n \in A$ for some positive integer n (depending on r). Show that A' is an ideal in R. In what way is this result a generalization of that of the preceding exercise?

6. If a ring R is imbedded in a ring S with unity by the method described in Section 2, prove that any ideal (right ideal) in R is also an ideal (right ideal) in S.

7. If R is a given ring, show that the set $\{i \mid i \in I, ia = 0 \text{ for every } a \in R\}$ is an ideal in the ring I of integers. Note that the nonnegative generator of this ideal is the characteristic of R.

8. In the ring I, verify that $(2) \cup (3)$ is not an ideal.

9. If A, B, and C are right ideals in a ring R such that $A \subseteq B \cup C$, show that $A \subseteq B$ or $A \subseteq C$.

10. In a complete matrix ring R_n, verify that the set of all matrices for which a certain prescribed set of rows consist entirely of zeros is a right ideal.

11. Verify that in the ring I_2 of all matrices of order two over the ring of integers the set of all matrices of the form

$$\begin{bmatrix} a - 2b & b \\ 2a - 4b & 2b \end{bmatrix}, \qquad a, b \in I,$$

is a right ideal.

12. If A is an ideal (right ideal) in the ring R, show that the complete matrix ring A_n is an ideal (right ideal) in the complete matrix ring R_n.

13. If A is an ideal (right ideal) in the ring R, show that the polynomial ring $A[x]$ is an ideal (right ideal) in the polynomial ring $R[x]$.

14. Prove 2.6 and 2.7.

15. Prove Theorem 2.8 (ii) and (iii).

16. Let S be the ring of all subsets of a given set A, as defined in Section 1. Prove each of the following:

(i) If B is a fixed subset of A, the set of all subsets of A which contain no element of B is an ideal in S.

(ii) If A has an infinite number of elements, the set T of all finite subsets of A is a proper ideal in S.

17. Prove that if R is a ring with more than one element such that $aR = R$ for every nonzero element a of R, then R is a division ring.

$\checkmark$**18.** If R is a commutative ring with unity, prove that an element $f(x)$ of $R[x]$ has an inverse in $R[x]$ if and only if the constant term of $f(x)$ has an inverse in R and all other coefficients of $f(x)$ are nilpotent.

7. SUMS AND DIRECT SUMS OF IDEALS

In this section we shall define and discuss the operation of addition on the set of ideals (right ideals) in a ring R.

If A_1 and A_2 are ideals (right ideals) in a ring R, we define

2.10 $$A_1 + A_2 = \{a_1 + a_2 \mid a_1 \in A_1, a_2 \in A_2\}.$$

It follows easily that $A_1 + A_2$ is an ideal (right ideal) in R. Since every ideal (right ideal) contains the zero element of R, we see that $A_1 \subseteq (A_1 + A_2)$ and $A_2 \subseteq (A_1 + A_2.)$ Moreover, any ideal (right ideal) which contains A_1 and A_2 must contain $A_1 + A_2$. We pointed out in 2.9, Exercise 8, that the union of two ideals need not be an ideal. We now observe that $A_1 + A_2$ is the ideal (right ideal) generated by the union $A_1 \cup A_2$ of A_1 and A_2. An alternative notation for $A_1 + A_2$ is (A_1, A_2), and it is frequently also called the *join* as well as the *sum* of A_1 and A_2.

The associative law of addition of elements of R easily implies that addition of ideals (right ideals), as defined in 2.10, also is associative. The sum of any finite number of ideals (right ideals) may be defined in the obvious way. If A_i $(i = 1, 2, \ldots, n)$ are ideals (right ideals) in R, we define the sum $A_1 + A_2 + \cdots + A_n$ $\left(\text{or } \sum_{i=1}^{n} A_i\right)$ to be the set of all sums

$$\sum_{i=1}^{n} a_i, \qquad a_i \in A_i; i = 1, 2, \ldots, n.$$

This ideal (right ideal) $\sum_{i=1}^{n} A_i$ is also called the join of the ideals (right ideals) A_i $(i = 1, 2, \ldots, n)$ and designated by $(A_1, A_2, \ldots, A_n)$. Of course, it is the ideal (right ideal) generated by the union of the ideals (right ideals) A_i $(i = 1, 2, \ldots, n)$.

It is sometimes desirable to extend the concept of sum (or join) to an arbitrary set of ideals (right ideals) in R. Suppose that $\mathfrak{A}$ is a set, finite or infinite, and that to each element i of $\mathfrak{A}$ there is associated an ideal (right ideal) A_i of R. This is sometimes expressed by saying that A_i, $i \in \mathfrak{A}$, is a family of ideals (right ideals) *indexed by the set* $\mathfrak{A}$. In the preceding paragraph, the finite set $\{1, 2, \ldots, n\}$ played the role of the set $\mathfrak{A}$. For future use, we may here observe that it is customary to denote the intersection of all the ideals (right ideals) A_i, $i \in \mathfrak{A}$, by

$$\bigcap_{i \in \mathfrak{A}} A_i,$$

and their union by

$$\bigcup_{i \in \mathfrak{A}} A_i.$$

The intersection is, of course, an ideal (right ideal) in R. The ideal (right ideal) generated by the union is called the sum (or join) of the ideals (right ideals) A_i, $i \in \mathfrak{A}$. It is easy to verify that it consists of all finite sums of the form $\sum a_i$, $(a_i \in A_i, i \in \mathfrak{A})$. Although we may have occasion to refer to the sum of an infinite number of ideals (right ideals), it may be emphasized that only *finite* sums of elements of R are involved.

The ideal A generated by a finite set $\{a_1, a_2, \ldots, a_n\}$ of elements of R is denoted by $(a_1, a_2, \ldots, a_n)$, and A is said to have the *finite basis* $\{a_1, a_2, \ldots, a_n\}$. A principal ideal is therefore the special case of an ideal with a basis of one element. It may be verified that

2.11 $$(a_1, a_2, \ldots, a_n) = (a_1) + (a_2) + \cdots + (a_n).$$

Similar remarks hold for right ideals with the appropriate modification of the notation. The concept of a basis is particularly useful in the study of commutative rings.

We now make the following definition.

2.12 Definition. A sum $A = \sum\limits_{i=1}^{n} A_i$ of a finite number of ideals (right ideals) in a ring R is called a *direct sum* provided each element of A is *uniquely* expressible in the form $\sum\limits_{i=1}^{n} a_i$, $(a_i \in A_i; i = 1, 2, \ldots, n)$. If the sum A is a direct sum, we may indicate this fact by writing $A = A_1 \oplus A_2 \oplus \cdots \oplus A_n$.

The next result gives conditions under which a sum is a direct sum.

2.13   Theorem.   *Let A_i $(i = 1, 2, \ldots, n)$ be ideals (right ideals) in a ring R. Then each of the following is true:*

(1) $\sum\limits_{i=1}^{n} A_i$ *is a direct sum if and only if* $\sum\limits_{i=1}^{n} a_i = 0$ $(a_i \in A_i; i = 1, 2,$ *..., n) implies that each $a_i = 0$ $(i = 1, 2, \ldots, n)$.*

(2) $\sum\limits_{i=1}^{n} A_i$ *is a direct sum if and only if for each $j = 1, 2, \ldots, n$,*

$$A_j \cap \left(\sum_{i \neq j} A_i \right) = (0).$$

In order to simplify our statements, let us agree that lower case letters with a subscript i are to be elements of A_i $(i = 1, 2, \ldots, n)$.

Proof of **(1)**: Suppose that $\sum\limits_{i=1}^{n} A_i$ is a direct sum and that $\sum\limits_{i=1}^{n} a_i = 0$. Since $0 \in A_i$ $(i = 1, 2, \ldots, n)$, the uniqueness property of a direct sum implies that each $a_i = 0$. Conversely, suppose that $\sum\limits_{i=1}^{n} a_i = 0$ implies that each $a_i = 0$. If $\sum\limits_{i=1}^{n} b_i = \sum\limits_{i=1}^{n} c_i$, then $\sum\limits_{i=1}^{n} (b_i - c_i) = 0$. Since $b_i - c_i \in A_i$, it follows that $b_i - c_i = 0$ or $b_i = c_i$ $(i = 1, 2, \ldots, n)$. Hence the sum is a direct sum by Definition 2.12.

Proof of **(2)**: Assume, first, that $\sum\limits_{i=1}^{n} A_i$ is a direct sum. Let j be a fixed integer from the set $\{1, 2, \ldots, n\}$, and suppose that a_j is an element of $A_j \cap \left(\sum\limits_{i \neq j} A_i \right)$. Then a_j is expressible in the form

$$a_j = a_1 + \cdots + a_{j-1} + a_{j+1} + \cdots + a_n,$$

and we have

$$a_1 + \cdots + a_{j-1} - a_j + a_{j+1} + \cdots + a_n = 0.$$

Since $-a_j \in A_j$, part (1) of the theorem assures us that all $a_i = 0$. In particular, $a_j = 0$ and therefore $A_j \cap \left(\sum\limits_{i \neq j} A_i \right) = (0)$. Conversely, let us assume that $A_j \cap \left(\sum\limits_{i \neq j} A_i \right) = (0)$, $(j = 1, 2, \ldots, n)$, and suppose that

$\sum\limits_{i=1}^{n} b_i = 0$. It follows that for each $j = 1, 2, \ldots, n$, we have

$$-b_j = b_1 + \cdots + b_{j-1} + b_{j+1} + \cdots + b_n.$$

Since the right side is an element of $\sum\limits_{i \neq j} A_i$ and $-b_j \in A_j$, it follows from our assumption that $b_j = 0$. Accordingly, $\sum\limits_{i=1}^{n} b_i = 0$ implies that all $b_i = 0$, and the desired result follows from part (1) of the theorem.

We may point out that the condition $A_j \cap \left(\sum\limits_{i \neq j} A_i \right) = (0)$ certainly implies that $A_j \cap A_k = (0)$ for $j \neq k$, but the converse is not generally true. However, in the special case in which $n = 2$ these two conditions are clearly equivalent and part (2) of the theorem then asserts that *a sum $A_1 + A_2$ of two ideals (right ideals) is a direct sum if and only if $A_1 \cap A_2 = (0)$.*

In the preceding chapter, we introduced the concept of direct sum of a given set of *rings*. It was pointed out in Example 3 of the preceding section that the direct sum $S = S_1 \oplus S_2 \oplus \cdots \oplus S_n$ of given rings S_i $(i = 1, 2, \ldots, n)$ contains two-sided ideals U_i such that $U_i \cong S_i$ $(i = 1, 2, \ldots, n)$. Moreover,

$$(a_1, a_2, \ldots, a_n) = (a_1, 0, 0, \ldots, 0) + (0, a_2, 0, \ldots, 0)$$
$$+ \cdots + (0, 0, \ldots, a_n)$$

is a unique expression of an element of S as a sum of elements of the respective ideals $U_1, U_2, \ldots, U_n$. Accordingly, in S the sum $\sum\limits_{i=1}^{n} U_i$ is a direct sum and in the notation of the present chapter we would write $S = U_1 \oplus U_2 \oplus \cdots \oplus U_n$. The close relation between these two kinds of direct sums will be explored further in 2.18, Exercise 13. Suffice it to say that the concept of direct sum of two-sided ideals, as defined in this section, essentially coincides with the concept of direct sum of rings as defined earlier. There can never be any confusion since in one case we start with a given set of rings and construct a ring which we call the direct sum of the given rings, and in the other case we start with ideals in a given ring and (if the proper conditions are satisfied) construct an ideal in the given ring which we call the direct sum of these ideals.

We next proceed to introduce an operation of multiplication on the set of ideals (right ideals) in a given ring.

8. IDEAL PRODUCTS AND NILPOTENT IDEALS

If A and B are ideals (right ideals) in a ring R, we define the product AB as follows:

$$2.14 \qquad\qquad AB = \{\sum a_i b_i \mid a_i \in A,\, b_i \in B\},$$

it being understood that all finite sums of one or more terms are to be included. It is easily verified that AB is an ideal (right ideal), and is in fact the ideal (right ideal) generated by the set of all products of the form ab, $a \in A$ and $b \in B$.

If A and B are two-sided ideals, each product ab, $a \in A$, $b \in B$, is in both A and B. Hence, for two-sided ideals we see that $AB \subseteq A \cap B$. If A and B are right ideals, $AB \subseteq A$, but it is not necessarily true that $AB \subseteq B$.

A special case of 2.14 of some interest is that in which B is a right ideal in R and $A = R$. It is easy to verify that RB is a two-sided ideal in R. In particular, if $a \in R$ we see that $R(aR)$, which we write simply as RaR, is a two-sided ideal in R. In this notation, if R has a unity, 2.7 may be expressed in the form $(a) = RaR$.

The multiplication 2.14 of ideals (right ideals) is easily shown to be associative. In the usual way, we denote AA by A^2; in general, for each positive integer $n > 1$, we define $A^n = A(A^{n-1})$.

2.15 Definition.   If A is an ideal (right ideal) such that $A^n = (0)$ for some positive integer n, A is said to be a *nilpotent* ideal (right ideal). If every element of A is nilpotent, A is said to be a *nil* ideal (right ideal).

We may emphasize that if A is nilpotent, there exists a positive integer n such that *every* product $a_1 a_2 \cdots a_n$ of n (distinct or identical) elements of A is zero. Certainly, then, a nilpotent ideal (right ideal) is a nil ideal (right ideal). We give an example to show that the converse need not be true. Let p be a fixed prime, and for each positive integer i let R_i be the ideal in $I/(p^{i+1})$, consisting of all nilpotent elements of $I/(p^{i+1})$, that is, consisting of the residue classes modulo p^{i+1} which contain multiples of p. Then $R_i^{i+1} = (0)$, whereas $R_i^k \neq (0)$ for $k < i + 1$. Now consider the discrete direct sum T of the rings R_i ($i = 1, 2, 3, \ldots$). Since each element of T differs from zero in only a finite number of components, each element of T is nilpotent and T is therefore a nil ideal in T or, as usually said, T is a nil ring. However, for each positive integer n there exist elements a of T such that $a^n \neq 0$. In other words, although every element of T is nilpotent there is no fixed positive integer n such that $a^n = 0$ for every $a \in T$. Accordingly, T is not nilpotent.

If R is a given ring, $R^2 = (0)$ clearly means that *every* product of elements of R is zero. We may sometimes explicitly exclude this trivial case by assuming that $R^2 \neq (0)$. Clearly, if R has a unity, $AR = A$ for every right ideal A; in particular, $R^2 = R$.

In a commutative ring R the set of all nilpotent elements is an ideal in R, but this need not be true in a noncommutative ring. (See 2.18, Exercise 3 and 1.13, Exercise 10.) However, the following result is of interest in this connection. We may emphasize that we are here considering two-sided ideals.

2.16 Theorem. *Let R be an arbitrary ring, and let us set*

2.17 $N = \{a \mid a \in R, (a)$ *is a nil ideal in* $R\}$.

Then N is a nil ideal which contains every nil ideal in R.

Proof: For $a \in N$ and $r \in R$, $ar \in (a)$ and therefore $(ar) \subseteq (a)$. Hence (ar) is a nil ideal and $ar \in N$. Similarly, $ra \in N$. To prove that N is an ideal, there remains to show that N is closed under subtraction. Accordingly, let $b, c \in N$ and let us show that $b - c \in N$. If $u \in (b - c)$, it follows from 2.6 that u is expressible in the form

$$u = b_1 + c_1,$$

where $b_1 \in (b)$ and $c_1 \in (c)$. Since (b) is a nil ideal, there exists a positive integer n such that $b_1^n = 0$. Now $u^n = (b_1 + c_1)^n$ can be expressed as b_1^n plus a sum of products each of which contains at least one element of (c_1). Since $(c_1) \subseteq (c)$, and $b_1^n = 0$, we see that $u^n \in (c)$ and u^n is therefore nilpotent. Accordingly, there exists a positive integer m such that $(u^n)^m = u^{nm} = 0$. This shows that every element u of $(b - c)$ is nilpotent and therefore that $(b - c)$ is a nil ideal. It follows that N is an ideal, as we wished to show; and clearly N is a nil ideal.

It is almost obvious that N contains every nil ideal of R. For if $s \in M$, where M is a nil ideal, then (s) is a nil ideal since $(s) \subseteq M$, and therefore $s \in N$ by the definition of N.

The ideal N, defined by 2.17, is sometimes called the (unique) *largest nil ideal* in R.

2.18 EXERCISES

1. Let k be the least common multiple and d the greatest common divisor of the integers m and n. In the ring I, verify each of the following: $(m) \cap (n) = (k)$; $(m, n) = (m) + (n) = (d)$; $(m)(n) = (mn)$.

2. If A, B, and C are right ideals in a ring R, prove that $A(B + C) = AB + AC$.

3. If R is a commutative ring, verify that the largest nil ideal in R consists of all nilpotent elements of R. Show by an example that this need not be true if R is not commutative.

4. Prove that if N is the largest nil ideal in the commutative ring R, then $N[x]$ is the largest nil ideal in the polynomial ring $R[x]$.

5. If, in 2.14, A is a left ideal and B is a right ideal, show that AB is a two-sided ideal. In Example 2 of Section 6, verify that $VU = K_2$.

6. If a is an element of an arbitrary ring R, show that $(a) = (a)_r + R(a)_r$.

7. Prove 2.11.

8. Let K be the set of all real numbers x such that $0 \le x \le 1$, and let R be the ring of all subsets of K. If a is the element of R which consists of all real numbers x such that $0 \le x \le 1/2$ and $b = \{1/4, 3/4\}$, describe each of the following ideals in R: (a), (b), (a, b), $(a)(b)$.

9. Let R be a ring with the property that if a right ideal A in R is such that $A^2 = (0)$, then $A = (0)$. Prove that R contains no nonzero nilpotent right ideals.

10. Prove that if a ring R contains a nonzero idempotent e such that e is not a left unity of R, then R is the direct sum of the nonzero right ideals eR and $\{a - ea \mid a \in R\}$.

11. Let A, B, and C be right ideals in a ring R. If $A \subseteq C$, prove that $A + (B \cap C) = (A + B) \cap C$.

12. Prove that the ideal T of 2.9, Exercise 16 (ii), does not have a finite basis.

13. Let $A = A_1 \oplus A_2 \oplus \cdots \oplus A_n$ be a direct sum of two-sided ideals in a ring R. Let B be the direct sum of the *rings* A_i as defined in Section 5, that is, the elements of B are of the form

$$(a_1, a_2, \ldots, a_n), \qquad\qquad a_i \in A_i,$$

with componentwise addition and multiplication. Show that the mapping

$$a_1 + a_2 + \cdots + a_n \to (a_1, a_2, \ldots, a_n)$$

is an isomorphism of A onto B.

9. SOME CONDITIONS ON IDEALS

We begin this section by making the following two definitions.

2.19 Definition.   An ideal (right ideal) A in a ring R is called a *minimal* ideal (right ideal) if $A \neq (0)$ and there exists no ideal (right ideal) B in R such that $(0) \subset B \subset A$.

2.20 Definition.   An ideal (right ideal) A in a ring R is called a *maximal* ideal (right ideal) if $A \neq R$ and there exists no ideal (right ideal) B in R such that $A \subset B \subset R$.

If a is an element of a right ideal A, then $(a)_r \subseteq A$. It follows that a nonzero right ideal is a minimal right ideal if and only if $(a)_r = A$ for *every* nonzero element a of A.

If A is a right ideal in R and $c \in R$, the right ideal generated by the set $A \cup \{c\}$ is often denoted by $(A, c)_r$. If $c \notin A$, clearly $A \subset (A, c)_r$. Hence a right ideal $A \neq R$ is a maximal right ideal in R if and only if $(A, c)_r = R$ for every element c of R which is not an element of A.

We may observe that since any right ideal which contains c actually contains $(c)_r$, we have

$$(A, c)_r = (A, (c)_r) = A + (c)_r.$$

The conditions which we have formulated above in order for a right ideal to be a minimal or a maximal right ideal are easily modified so as to apply to two-sided ideals. As to notation, if A is an ideal in R and $c \in R$, the ideal generated by the set $A \cup \{c\}$ is often denoted by (A, c), as well as by $(A, (c))$ or by $A + (c)$.

We now illustrate these concepts by examples.

EXAMPLE 1.   In the ring I of integers, we proved in Theorem 2.8 that every ideal is a principal ideal generated by a nonnegative integer. If m and n are positive integers, clearly $(m) \subset (n)$ if and only if $m = nk$ for some integer $k > 1$. It follows easily that in I there are no minimal ideals. However, an ideal (m) is a maximal ideal in I if and only if m is a prime integer.

EXAMPLE 2.   Consider the ring D_n of all matrices of order n over a division ring D. Let k be an integer from the set $\{1, 2, \ldots, n\}$, and let $A(k)$ be the right ideal in D_n consisting of all those matrices of D_n

having only zeros in all rows except possibly the kth row. We shall show that $A(k)$ is a minimal right ideal in D_n.

The elements of $A(k)$ are of the form

$$2.21 \qquad \sum_{j=1}^{n} a_{kj}E_{kj}, \qquad a_{kj} \in D; \quad j = 1, 2, \ldots, n.$$

Let

$$M = \sum_{t=1}^{n} b_{kt}E_{kt}$$

be an arbitrary nonzero element of $A(k)$, so that for at least one integer q, $b_{kq} \neq 0$. We shall show that the right ideal $(M)_r$ in D_n generated by the element M contains an arbitrary element 2.21 of $A(k)$, and hence that $(M)_r = A(k)$. For a fixed j, we have (using 1.24)

$$Mb_{kq}^{-1}a_{kj}E_{qj} = \sum_{t=1}^{n} b_{kt}b_{kq}^{-1}a_{kj}E_{kt}E_{qj}$$
$$= a_{kj}E_{kj}.$$

This shows that $a_{kj}E_{kj} \in (M)_r$ and hence the sum 2.21 also is an element of $(M)_r$. Therefore, $(M)_r = A(k)$, and $A(k)$ is a minimal right ideal in D_n.

The following condition will play an important role at various points in later chapters.

2.22 **Definition.** If for a ring R every strictly decreasing sequence of right ideals in R,

$$A_1 \supset A_2 \supset A_3 \supset \cdots$$

contains only a finite number of right ideals, we say that the *descending chain condition* for right ideals holds in R.

An alternate, and sometimes useful, formulation of the descending chain condition for right ideals is as follows. In any infinite sequence of right ideals such that

$$A_1 \supseteq A_2 \supseteq A_3 \supseteq \cdots$$

there exists a positive integer n such that $A_n = A_{n+1} = A_{n+2} = \cdots$.
It is easy to verify (cf. 2.29, Exercise 8) that the descending chain

condition for right ideals in a ring R is equivalent to the condition that in every nonempty set of right ideals in R there exists a right ideal which is minimal in the set (in the sense that it properly contains no other right ideal of the set). A minimal right ideal in R, as defined in 2.19, is a right ideal which is minimal in the set of all *nonzero* right ideals of R. We saw in Example 1 that there are rings which do not contain any minimal right ideals. However, if the descending chain condition for right ideals holds in a ring R, then R necessarily contains one or more minimal right ideals.

For the sake of completeness, we make the following definition although we shall not have much occasion to use it.

2.23 Definition. If for a ring R every strictly increasing sequence of right ideals in R,

$$A_1 \subset A_2 \subset A_3 \subset \cdots$$

contains only a finite number of right ideals, we say that the *ascending chain condition* for right ideals holds in R.

Equivalent formulations can easily be given as in the case of the descending chain condition. In particular, we may point out that a maximal right ideal, as defined in 2.20, is a right ideal which is maximal in the set of all right ideals other than R itself.

We shall usually abbreviate "descending chain condition" to "d.c.c." and "ascending chain condition" to "a.c.c."

We have formulated Definitions 2.22 and 2.23 for *right* ideals since they will be our primary interest, but it will be obvious how to define the d.c.c. and the a.c.c. for left ideals or for ideals.

EXAMPLE 3. The d.c.c. for ideals does not hold in the ring I of integers since I contains no minimal ideals. However, since $(n) \subset (m)$ if and only if m is a divisor of n, it follows that the a.c.c. for ideals does hold in I.

EXAMPLE 4. Let S be the complete direct sum of an infinite number of nonzero rings R_i $(i = 1, 2, 3, \ldots)$. For each positive integer k, let P_k be the set of all elements of S for which the first k components are zero. Then P_k is an ideal in S and we have the infinite decreasing sequence of ideals

$$P_1 \supset P_2 \supset P_3 \supset \cdots.$$

Therefore, the d.c.c. for ideals does not hold in S. Now let Q_k be the set of all elements of S for which all components *except* possibly the first k are zero. Then each Q_k is an ideal in S and we have the infinite increasing sequence of ideals

$$Q_1 \subset Q_2 \subset Q_3 \subset \cdots,$$

so that the a.c.c. for ideals also does not hold in S. If, as a special case, the rings R_i are fields so that in R_i the only ideals are R_i and the zero ideal, it is not difficult to show that P_1 is a maximal ideal in S and Q_1 is a minimal ideal in S. We have thus an example of a ring which has minimal ideals and maximal ideals but in which neither of the chain conditions holds.

In the preceding section we showed by an example that a nil ideal need not be nilpotent. In a later chapter we shall prove the rather remarkable fact that if the d.c.c. for right ideals holds in a ring R, every nil right ideal in R is necessarily nilpotent.

10. IDEALS IN COMPLETE MATRIX RINGS

In this section we shall prove an important result about (two-sided) ideals in complete matrix rings.

If M is an ideal in the ring R, it is known (see 2.9, Exercise 12) that the ring M_n of all matrices of order n over M is an ideal in the ring R_n of all matrices of order n over R. The following theorem gives a partial converse to this result.

2.24 Theorem. *If R has a unity, every ideal in the complete matrix ring R_n is of the form M_n, where M is an ideal in R.*

Proof: Let $\mathfrak{M}$ be an ideal in R_n, and let M be the set of all elements of R that occur in the first row and first column of matrices in $\mathfrak{M}$. We shall establish the theorem by showing that M is an ideal in R and that $\mathfrak{M} = M_n$.

Since $\mathfrak{M}$ is closed under addition (and subtraction), the same is true of M. If $m \in M$ and $r \in R$, let us show that $mr \in M$. By definition of M, there exists an element $\sum m_{ij}E_{ij}$ of $\mathfrak{M}$ with $m_{11} = m$. Then, using Formulas 1.24 for multiplication of the matrix units, it follows that

$$E_{11}(\sum m_{ij}E_{ij})(rE_{11}) = mrE_{11} \in \mathfrak{M}.$$

Now mrE_{11} has mr in the first row and first column (and zeros elsewhere), so $mr \in M$. Similarly, $rm \in M$ and M is an ideal in R.

As an aid in completing the proof, we first make the following observation. Let r, s, p, and q be integers from the set $\{1, 2, \ldots, n\}$. If $A = \sum a_{ij}E_{ij}$ is an element of R_n, then

2.25 $$E_{pr}AE_{sq} = E_{pr}(\sum a_{ij}E_{ij})E_{sq} = a_{rs}E_{pq}.$$

Thus, $E_{pr}AE_{sq}$ is the matrix with a_{rs} in the pth row and q^{th} column and zeros elsewhere.

Suppose, now, that $A \in \mathfrak{M}$ and let us show that $A \in M_n$. By 2.25 with $p = q = 1$, we see that $a_{rs}E_{11} \in \mathfrak{M}$ and so $a_{rs} \in M$. Since this is true for all $r, s = 1, 2, \ldots, n$, it follows that $A \in M_n$. We have therefore shown that $\mathfrak{M} \subseteq M_n$.

Now let $B = \sum b_{ij}E_{ij}$ be an element of M_n. By definition of M, if p and q are any integers from the set $\{1, 2, \ldots, n\}$, there exists an element $A = \sum a_{ij}E_{ij}$ of $\mathfrak{M}$ such that $a_{11} = b_{pq}$. By applying 2.25 with $r = s = 1$, we see that $b_{pq}E_{pq} \in \mathfrak{M}$. But B is a sum of such matrices, and therefore $B \in \mathfrak{M}$. It follows that $M_n \subseteq \mathfrak{M}$, and the proof of the theorem is completed.

If R does not have a unity, the above proof breaks down since we do not have as elements of R_n the matrix units E_{pr}, E_{sq} occurring in 2.25. Actually, the conclusion of the theorem is not necessarily true if R does not have a unity. (See 2.29, Exercise 6.)

It will be convenient to have the following definition before stating a few consequences of the theorem just established.

2.26 Definition. A ring R with more than one element is said to be a *simple ring* if its only ideals are the two trivial ideals, namely, (0) and R.

We may point out that since R^2 is an ideal in R, for a simple ring R the condition $R^2 \neq (0)$ is equivalent to the condition $R^2 = R$.

The following corollary is an immediate consequence of Theorem 2.24.

2.27   Corollary. *If R is a simple ring with unity, so is the complete matrix ring R_n^* for each positive integer n.*

It is clear that a division ring is necessarily simple. This special case of the preceding result is of such importance that we state it explicitly.

2.28   Corollary. *If D is a division ring and n is a positive integer, the complete matrix ring D_n is simple.*

2.29   EXERCISES : ⤳

1. Show that there are no minimal ideals in a polynomial ring $F[x]$, where F is a field. Determine all maximal ideals in this ring. Do either of the chain conditions for ideals hold in this ring?

2. Show that in the ring $F[[x]]$ of formal power series over a field there are no minimal ideals and exactly one maximal ideal. Do either of the chain conditions for ideals hold in this ring?

3. Verify that the minimal right ideal $A(k)$ of Example 2 of Section 9 is the principal right ideal generated by an idempotent element of D_n.

4. In the notation of Example 2 of Section 9 show that

$$D_n = A(1) \oplus A(2) \oplus \cdots \oplus A(n).$$

5. If D is a division ring, express the complete matrix ring D_n as a direct sum of minimal *left* ideals.

6. Let E be the ring of all even integers. Verify that in the complete matrix ring E_2 the set of all matrices of the form

$$\begin{bmatrix} a & b \\ c & d \end{bmatrix}$$

in which a is divisible by 4 is an ideal.

7. Find a minimal ideal and a maximal ideal in the ring R of 2.18, Exercise 8. Show that neither the d.c.c. nor the a.c.c. for ideals holds in this ring.

8. Prove that the d.c.c. for right ideals holds in a ring R if and only if in every nonempty set of right ideals of R there is a right ideal which is minimal in this set. State and prove a corresponding result for the a.c.c.

9. Prove that if R is a ring with $R^2 \neq (0)$ and such that R is a minimal right ideal in R, then R is a division ring.

10. Determine all simple commutative rings.

11. If A is a right ideal in a ring R and $r \in R$, then $rA = \{ra \mid a \in A\}$ is a right ideal in R. Prove that if A is a minimal right ideal in R and $rA \neq (0)$, then rA is also a minimal right ideal in R.

12. If the ring R has minimal right ideals, use the result of the preceding exercise to show that the sum of all the minimal right ideals in R is a two-sided ideal in R.

11. RESIDUE CLASS RINGS

Let N be a two-sided ideal in the ring R. If $a, b \in R$, we write $a \equiv b$ (mod N) (read "a is congruent to b modulo N") to mean that $a - b \in N$. It is easy to verify that this congruence modulo N is an equivalence relation on the set R. Moreover, if $a \equiv a_1$ (mod N) and $b \equiv b_1$ (mod N), then

2.30 $$a + b \equiv a_1 + b_1 \,(\text{mod } N)$$

and

2.31 $$ab \equiv a_1 b_1 \,(\text{mod } N).$$

We prove 2.31 and leave the proof of 2.30 to the reader. Since $a \equiv a_1$ (mod N) and $b \equiv b_1$ (mod N), there exist $n_1, n_2 \in N$ such that $a - a_1 = n_1$ and $b - b_1 = n_2$. It follows that

$$ab = (a_1 + n_1)(b_1 + n_2) = a_1 b_1 + a_1 n_2 + n_1 b_1 + n_1 n_2.$$

However, $a_1 n_2 + n_1 b_1 + n_1 n_2$ is an element of N since N is closed under multiplication by elements of R and under addition. Hence, $ab - a_1 b_1$ is an element of N, that is, $ab \equiv a_1 b_1$ (mod N).

If $a \in R$ and N is an ideal in R, let us define

$$a + N = \{a + n \mid n \in N\}.$$

With respect to the equivalence relation of congruence modulo N, the *residue class* (or *equivalence set*) which contains the element a is just the set $a + N$. Now let us define operations of addition and multiplication on the set of these residue classes as follows:

2.32 $$(a + N) + (b + N) = (a + b) + N,$$

and

2.33 $$(a + N)(b + N) = ab + N.$$

Since $a + N = a_1 + N$ if and only if $a \equiv a_1$ (mod N), Properties 2.30 and 2.31 show that addition and multiplication of residue classes are well-defined by 2.32 and 2.33, respectively. We may now state the following important theorem.

2.34 Theorem. *Let N be an ideal in the ring R. If addition and multiplication of residue classes modulo N are defined by 2.32 and 2.33 respectively, the set of all these residue classes is a ring. This ring is denoted by R/N and usually called a* residue class ring (*or a* quotient ring).

We shall leave the proof of this theorem as an exercise. However, we may observe that the zero of the ring R/N is the residue class N, the residue class which contains the zero of R.

Except possibly for notation, a special case of the above theorem should seem familiar. Let n be a positive integer and $N = (n)$ the principal ideal in the ring I of integers generated by n. Then congruence modulo the ideal N, as defined in this section, coincides with the well-known congruence modulo n. Moreover, the ring I/N is precisely the ring $I/(n)$ of integers modulo n.

Remark. Let R^+ denote the additive group of the ring R. If N^+ is a subgroup of R^+ and we define $a \equiv b \pmod{N^+}$ to mean that $a - b \in N^+$, then we have an equivalence relation on R^+ and we can proceed as above *insofar as addition is concerned.* The group whose elements are the *cosets* (equivalence sets) $a + N^+$, $a \in R^+$, with addition defined by

2.35 $$(a + N^+) + (b + N^+) = (a + b) + N^+$$

is often called a *difference group* and denoted by $R^+ - N^+$. Of course, any abelian (commutative) group with the operation written as addition may be used in place of the additive group of a ring. However, for our purposes, the case of most importance is that in which we have the additive group R^+ of a ring R, and the subgroup N^+ is the additive group of a right ideal in R.

2.36 EXERCISES

1. Prove that if N is an ideal (right ideal) in a ring R, then congruence modulo N is an equivalence relation on the set R.

2. Prove Theorem 2.34.

3. If F is a field and $s(x)$ is an element of $F[x]$ of positive degree, prove that the residue class ring $F[x]/(s(x))$ is a field if and only if $s(x)$ is a prime (irreducible) polynomial over F.

4. Let I be the ring of integers, R the field of rational numbers, K the field of real numbers, and let x and y be indeterminates. Determine a familiar ring which is isomorphic to each of the following residue class rings: $K[x]/(x^2 + 1)$, $I[x]/(x)$, $I[x]/(x^2 + 1)$, $R[x]/(x^2 - 2)$, $I[x]/(x, 3)$, $K[x, y]/(y)$.

5. Prove that if A and N are ideals in a ring R and $N \subseteq A$, then A/N is an ideal in R/N.

6. Let N be an ideal in the ring R, and S a subring of R such that $S \cap N = (0)$. Show that the mapping $s \to s + N$, $s \in S$, defines an isomorphism of S onto a subring of R/N.

7. If A is an ideal in the ring R, prove that the complete matrix ring $(R/A)_n$ is isomorphic to the ring R_n/A_n.

8. If N is the ideal of all nilpotent elements in a commutative ring R, show that the ring R/N contains no nonzero nilpotent elements.

9. Prove that if A is an ideal in R, then $(R/A)[x] \cong R[x]/A[x]$.

10. Let R be a ring without a unity and with no nonzero divisors of zero, and let T be the ring of all pairs (a, n), $a \in R$, $n \in I$, with addition and multiplication defined as in Section 2. Then T contains a subring isomorphic to R and a subring isomorphic to I. Define

$$A = \{(a, n) \mid (a, n) \in T, ar + nr = 0 \text{ for every } r \in R\}.$$

Prove each of the following:

(i) A is an ideal in T.

(ii) T/A has a unity and contains a subring isomorphic to R.

(iii) T/A contains no nonzero divisors of zero.

12. HOMOMORPHISMS

We now introduce some notation which will be useful in the study of mappings of a given set R into a given set S. A little later on we shall be concerned with certain important mappings for the case in which both R and S are *rings*.

We shall often find it convenient to denote a mapping by a Greek letter such as θ. If θ is a mapping of a set R into a set S, we may denote the image of an element a of R under the mapping θ by $a\theta$. We may also write $\theta: a \to a\theta$, $a \in R$, to indicate that θ is a mapping of the set R into some set which will be specified explicitly or be obvious from the context. To exhibit a mapping θ of the set R into the set S, it is clearly only necessary to specify the element $a\theta$ of S for each element a of R.

Now let θ be a mapping of the set R into the set S. If A is a subset of R, we denote by $A\theta$ the set of all elements of S that are images of elements of A under the mapping θ, that is,

$$A\theta = \{a\theta \mid a \in A\}.$$

In this notation, the given mapping θ of R into S is a mapping of R *onto* the subset $R\theta$ of S. Therefore, θ is a mapping of R onto S if and only if $S = R\theta$. It is clear that if A and B are subsets of R such that $A \subseteq B$, then $A\theta \subseteq B\theta$.

If U is a set of elements of S, we denote by $U\theta^{-1}$ the set of all elements of R whose images under the mapping θ are elements of U, that is,

$$U\theta^{-1} = \{r \mid r \in R, r\theta \in U\}.$$

We may emphasize that θ^{-1} is not a mapping of S into R, but it may be considered to be a mapping of subsets of S into subsets of R. If U and V are subsets of S such that $U \subseteq V$, it follows that $U\theta^{-1} \subseteq V\theta^{-1}$.

The mapping θ of the set R into the set S is a *one-one mapping* of R into S (onto $R\theta$) if and only if for $a, b \in R$, $a\theta = b\theta$ implies that $a = b$.

For ease of reference, we next state the following facts whose verification will be left as an exercise. It is to be understood that θ is a given mapping of a set R into a set S.

2.37   *If A is a subset of R, then $A \subseteq (A\theta)\theta^{-1}$.*

2.38   *If θ is a one-one mapping, for each subset A of R we have $A = (A\theta)\theta^{-1}$.*

2.39   *If U is a subset of S, then $U \supseteq (U\theta^{-1})\theta$.*

2.40   *If θ is a mapping of R onto S (that is, if $S = R\theta$), for each subset U of S we have $U = (U\theta^{-1})\theta$.*

We henceforth restrict attention to the case in which R and S are rings, and make the following important definition.

2.41   Definition.   A mapping θ of a ring R into a ring S is said to be a *homomorphism of R into S* if addition and multiplication are preserved under this mapping, that is, if for $a, b \in R$,

$$(a + b)\theta = a\theta + b\theta$$

and

$$(ab)\theta = (a\theta)(b\theta).$$

If there exists a homomorphism θ of R onto S (so that $R\theta = S$), we may say that R is *homomorphic to S* or that S is a *homomorphic image* of R.

Let us now list, without proof, a few elementary but fundamental properties of homomorphisms. If θ is a homomorphism of a ring R into a ring S, each of the following is true:

2.42

(i) If 0 is the zero of R, then 0θ is the zero of S.

(ii) If $a \in R$, then $(-a)\theta = -(a\theta)$.

(iii) $R\theta$ is a subring of S.

(iv) If R has a unity 1, then the ring $R\theta$ has 1θ as unity.

(v) If R is a commutative ring, the ring $R\theta$ is also commutative.

Since $R\theta$ is a ring (by 2.42(iii)), it follows that if θ is a homomorphism of R into S, then θ is a homomorphism of R onto the ring $R\theta$. We may sometimes say that S *contains* the homomorphic image $R\theta$ of R.

An isomorphism, as defined in 1.12, is clearly the special case of a homomorphism in which the mapping is a one-one mapping. Thus a homomorphism θ is an isomorphism if and only if $a\theta = b\theta$ implies that $a = b$.

We next make another definition as follows.

2.43 Definition. If θ is a homomorphism of a ring R into a ring S, then $(0)\theta^{-1}$, that is, the set of all elements a of R such that $a\theta = 0$ (the zero of S), is called the *kernel* of the homomorphism θ.

It is clear from 2.42(i) that the kernel of an *isomorphism* is zero (that is, is the set $\{0\}$). Conversely, *if the kernel of a homomorphism θ is zero, θ is necessarily an isomorphism.* For if $a\theta = b\theta$, it follows from 2.42(ii) and the fact that addition is preserved under the mapping θ that $(a - b)\theta = a\theta - b\theta = 0$. Hence $a - b$ is in the kernel of θ and therefore $a - b = 0$. Thus $a = b$, and θ is a one-one mapping.

If N is an ideal in the ring R, Definitions 2.32 and 2.33 of addition and multiplication in the residue class ring R/N make it apparent that the mapping $\theta: a\theta = a + N$, $a \in R$, of R onto R/N is a homomorphism of R onto R/N. There might very well exist other homomorphisms of R onto R/N but this one is often called the *natural* homomorphism of R onto R/N. In this natural homomorphism of R onto R/N, $a\theta = 0$ if and only if $a + N = N$ (since N is the zero of the ring R/N), and this is true if and only if $a \in N$. That is, the kernel of this homomorphism is the ideal N.

It is an important fact that, in a certain sense, every homomorphism of a ring R *onto* a ring S is of the type described in the preceding paragraph. A precise statement of this result is as follows.

2.44   Fundamental Theorem on Homomorphisms.   *Let θ be a homomorphism of the ring R onto the ring $S = R\theta$, with kernel K. Then K is an ideal in R and $S \cong R/K$. In fact, the mapping α: $(a\theta)\alpha = a + K$, $a \in R$, is an isomorphism of S onto R/K.*

Proof: Let us first prove that K is an ideal in R. If a, $b \in K$, then $a\theta = 0$ and $b\theta = 0$, and it follows readily that $(a - b)\theta = 0$. Hence, $a - b \in K$. Moreover, if $a \in K$ and $r \in R$, we have $(ar)\theta = (a\theta)(r\theta) = 0(r\theta) = 0$, so that $ar \in K$. A similar calculation shows that also $ra \in K$, and K is therefore an ideal in R.

Since θ is a mapping of R onto S, every element of S is of the form $a\theta$, $a \in R$. However, since many different elements of R may have the same image under the mapping θ, it is essential to show that α is a well-defined mapping of S onto R/K. Suppose that a, $b \in R$ such that $a\theta = b\theta$. Then $(a - b)\theta = 0$, or $a - b \in K$. Thus $a \equiv b \pmod{K}$, and this implies that $a + K = b + K$. Therefore, the mapping α is well defined and it is clearly a mapping *onto* R/K. Simple calculations as follows, using the fact that θ is a homomorphism and the definitions of addition and multiplication in R/K, show that addition and multiplication are preserved under the mapping α of S onto R/K:

$$(a\theta + b\theta)\alpha = [(a + b)\theta]\alpha = (a + b) + K$$
$$= (a + K) + (b + K)$$
$$= (a\theta)\alpha + (b\theta)\alpha,$$

$$[(a\theta)(b\theta)]\alpha = [(ab)\theta]\alpha = ab + K$$
$$= (a + K)(b + K)$$
$$= [(a\theta)\alpha][(b\theta)\alpha].$$

This shows that α is a homomorphism of S onto R/K, and there remains only to show that its kernel is zero. If $(a\theta)\alpha = 0$, then $a + K = K$, and $a \in K$. But since K is the kernel of the homomorphism θ, $a\theta = 0$ and the kernel of the homomorphism α is zero. Thus α is an isomorphism and the proof is completed.

One of the consequences of this theorem may be stated as follows. If isomorphic rings are not considered as "different," the *only* homomorphic images of a ring R are those which occur under natural homomorphisms of R onto residue class rings R/K. Accordingly, if we know all ideals K in R, we know all homomorphic images of R. For example, in the ring I of integers every ideal is a principal ideal (n), where n is a non-negative integer. Therefore, the rings which are homomorphic images of I are the rings (isomorphic to rings) of the form $I/(n)$.

Several important properties of homomorphisms are collected in the following theorem.

2.45   Theorem.   *Let θ be a homomorphism of the ring R onto the ring $S = R\theta$, with kernel K. Then each of the following is true:*

(i) *If A is an ideal (right ideal) in R, then $A\theta$ is an ideal (right ideal) in S.*

(ii) *If U is an ideal (right ideal) in S, then $U\theta^{-1}$ is an ideal (right ideal) in R which contains K.*

(iii) *If A is an ideal (right ideal) in R which contains K, then $A = (A\theta)\theta^{-1}$.*

(iv) *The mapping $A \to A\theta$ defines a one-one mapping of the set of all ideals (right ideals) in R which contain K onto the set of all ideals (right ideals) in S.*

(v) *If A and B are ideals (right ideals) in R which contain K, then $A \subset B$ if and only if $A\theta \subset B\theta$.*

We shall prove the last three parts of this theorem and leave the proofs of the first two parts as an exercise. We shall refer to ideals, but the same arguments apply to right ideals as well.

Proof of (iii): If $c \in (A\theta)\theta^{-1}$, then $c\theta \in A\theta$, and there exists an element a of A such that $c\theta = a\theta$. Hence $(c - a)\theta = 0$ and $c - a \in K$. Since $K \subseteq A$, it follows that $c \in A$. This shows that $(A\theta)\theta^{-1} \subseteq A$. But $A \subseteq (A\theta)\theta^{-1}$ by 2.37, and therefore $A = (A\theta)\theta^{-1}$.

Proof of (iv): If U is an arbitrary ideal in S, part (ii) asserts that $U\theta^{-1}$ is an ideal in R which contains K. Then, by 2.40, $(U\theta^{-1})\theta = U$, so the mapping is *onto*. To prove that it is one-one, suppose that A and B are ideals in R which contain K and such that $A\theta = B\theta$. Then, clearly, $(A\theta)\theta^{-1} = (B\theta)\theta^{-1}$, and part (iii) shows that $A = B$. This proves that the mapping is a one-one mapping.

Proof of (v): Suppose, first, that $A \subset B$. Then $A\theta \subseteq B\theta$. If $A\theta = B\theta$, then $A = B$, since $A \to A\theta$ is a one-one mapping by part (iv). Hence $A\theta \neq B\theta$, so $A\theta \subset B\theta$. Assume, next, that $A\theta \subset B\theta$. Then, by part (iii), we have $A = (A\theta)\theta^{-1} \subseteq (B\theta)\theta^{-1} = B$. Since $A\theta \subset B\theta$, we cannot have $A = B$, so we conclude that $A \subset B$. This completes the proof.

In applications of this theorem we may very well *start* with an arbitrary two-sided ideal K in R and let θ be the natural homomorphism $a \to a + K$ of R onto $S = R/K$. Of course, the kernel of this homomorphism is the given ideal K. If A is an ideal (right ideal) in R which contains K, then K is an ideal in the ring A and $A\theta = A/K$. Theorem 2.45 then shows that *each ideal (right ideal) in R/K is of the form A/K, where A is an ideal (right ideal) in R which contains K.* Moreover, we have a one-one mapping of the set of all ideals (right ideals) in R which contain K onto the set of all ideals (right ideals) in R/K. One particular consequence of this last observation is of such importance that we state it as the following corollary.

2.46   Corollary.   *A residue class ring R/K is a simple ring if and only if K is a maximal ideal in R.*

This result follows from the observation that R/K is a simple ring if and only if there are exactly two ideals (the trivial ones) in R/K, and K is a maximal ideal in R if and only if there are only two ideals (K and R) in R which contain K.

Another important theorem on homomorphisms is as follows.

2.47   Theorem.   *If θ is a homomorphism of the ring R onto the ring $S = R\theta$, with kernel K, and A is an ideal in R which contains K, then*

$$R/A \cong R\theta/A\theta.$$

Proof: We are given that $r \to r\theta$, $r \in R$, is a homomorphism of R onto S, and clearly $r\theta \to r\theta + A\theta$, $r\theta \in S$, is the natural homomorphism of S onto $S/A\theta$. It follows easily (see 2.50, Exercise 10) that

2.48 $$r \to r\theta + A\theta, \qquad\qquad r \in R,$$

is a homomorphism of R onto $S/A\theta$. Let us determine the kernel K' of this homomorphism 2.48. Now $r \in K'$ if and only if $r\theta + A\theta = 0$, that is, if and only if $r\theta \in A\theta$ or $r \in (A\theta)\theta^{-1}$. However, by Theorem 2.45 (iii), we have $A = (A\theta)\theta^{-1}$, so $K' = A$. By Theorem 2.44, we conclude that $R/A \cong S/A\theta$, and the proof is therefore completed.

Again, if we start with an ideal K in R and let θ be the natural homomorphism of R onto R/K, the last theorem takes the following form which we state explicitly for ease of reference.

2.49 Theorem. *If A and K are ideals in the ring R such that $K \subseteq A$, then*

$$R/A \cong (R/K)/(A/K).$$

2.50 EXERCISES

1. Prove 2.37 through 2.40.

2. Prove 2.42.

3. Let $F[x]$ be the ring of polynomials in an indeterminate x over a field F, and let a be a fixed element of F. Show that the mapping $\theta: f(x)\theta = f(a)$, $f(x) \in F[x]$, is a homomorphism of $F[x]$ onto F. What is the kernel of this homomorphism?

4. Let $F[x, y]$ be the ring of polynomials in indeterminates x and y over the field F. If a, $b \in F$, find a homomorphism of $F[x, y]$ onto F whose kernel is the ideal $(x - a, y - b)$. How do you know that this ideal is a maximal ideal in $F[x, y]$?

5. If θ is a homomorphism of the ring R onto the ring S and $a \in R$, prove that $(a)\theta = (a\theta)$ and that $(a)_r\theta = (a\theta)_r$. Prove also that if every ideal (right ideal) in R is a principal ideal (right ideal), then the same is true in S.

6. Prove Theorem 2.45 (i) and (ii).

7. Let θ be a homomorphism of the ring R onto the ring S. If A and B are ideals (right ideals) in R, and U and V are ideals (right ideals) in S, prove each of the following:

    (i) $(A + B)\theta = A\theta + B\theta$,

    (ii) $(AB)\theta = (A\theta)(B\theta)$,

    (iii) $(U + V)\theta^{-1} = U\theta^{-1} + V\theta^{-1}$,

    (iv) $(UV)\theta^{-1} \supseteq (U\theta^{-1})(V\theta^{-1})$.

8. Let S be a homomorphic image of R. Prove that if the d.c.c. for right ideals holds in R, it also holds in S. Show by an example that the converse of this statement need not be true.

9. Prove that if M is a maximal ideal in the commutative ring R with unity, then the ring R/M is a field.

10. If $r \to r\theta$, $r \in R$, is a homomorphism of a ring R onto a ring S, and $s \to s\phi$, $s \in S$, is a homomorphism of S onto a ring T, show that $r \to (r\theta)\phi$, $r \in R$, is a homomorphism of R onto T.

11. If N is the largest nil ideal in an arbitrary ring R, prove that the ring R/N contains no nonzero nil ideal.

12. Let M be a proper ideal in a Boolean ring B. Prove (i) that B/M is a Boolean ring, and (ii) that $B/M \cong I/(2)$ if and only if M is a maximal ideal in B.

13. Let $F[x]$ and $F[[x]]$ be, respectively, the ring of polynomials and the ring of formal power series in an indeterminate x over a field F. Prove that every ring which is a homomorphic, but not isomorphic, image of $F[[x]]$ is also a homomorphic image of $F[x]$.

14. If A and B are ideals in a ring R, prove that

$$(A + B)/B \cong A/(A \cap B).$$

15. Let us say that a right ideal A in a ring R is *R-isomorphic* to a right ideal B in R if there exists an isomorphism θ of the additive group of A onto the additive group of B and, moreover, for $a \in A$ and $s \in R$ we have $(as)\theta = (a\theta)s$. If A is a minimal right ideal in R and $r \in R$ such that $rA \neq (0)$, we know by 2.29, Exercise 11, that rA is a minimal right ideal of R. Prove that A is R-isomorphic to rA.

16. If a ring R has minimal right ideals, prove that the sum of all minimal right ideals of R which are R-isomorphic to some one minimal right ideal is a two-sided ideal in R.

CHAPTER 3

Subdirect Sums of Rings

IN SECTION 5 (Chapter 1) we defined the direct sum of a finite number of rings, and also the complete direct sum and discrete direct sum of a denumerably infinite set of rings. In this chapter we shall generalize these concepts by defining in a natural way the direct sum of an entirely arbitrary set of rings. We shall then consider in some detail certain important subrings of direct sums.

13. DEFINITIONS AND FUNDAMENTAL PROPERTIES

Let S_i, $i \in \mathfrak{A}$, be a family of rings indexed by the set $\mathfrak{A}$, and let us consider functions defined on $\mathfrak{A}$ such that at $i \in \mathfrak{A}$ the value of the function is in S_i. Thus, if a is such a function, $a(i) \in S_i$ for each $i \in \mathfrak{A}$. Sums and products of these functions are defined in the usual way as follows:

3.1 $$(a + b)(i) = a(i) + b(i), \quad (ab)(i) = (a(i))(b(i)).$$

It is easily verified that the set of all functions of the kind just described is a ring. We now make the following formal definition.

3.2 Definition. Let S_i, $i \in \mathfrak{A}$, be a given family of rings and let us denote by S the set of all functions defined on the set $\mathfrak{A}$ such that for each $i \in \mathfrak{A}$ the value of the function at i is an element of S_i. If addition and multiplication in S are defined by 3.1, then S is a ring which is called the *complete direct sum* of the rings S_i, $i \in \mathfrak{A}$. The set of all functions in S which take on the value zero at all but at most a finite number of elements i of $\mathfrak{A}$ is a subring of S which is called the *discrete direct sum* of the rings S_i, $i \in \mathfrak{A}$.

The special cases which have already been introduced in Chapter 1 arise if $\mathfrak{A} = \{1, 2, \ldots, n\}$ or if $\mathfrak{A}$ is the set of all positive integers. Let us consider again for a moment the direct sum S of a finite number of rings S_i $(i = 1, 2, \ldots, n)$. We formerly represented an element a of S as follows:

3.3 $$a = (a_1, a_2, \ldots, a_n), \quad a_i \in S_i; i = 1, 2, \ldots, n.$$

However, this element a defines the function on the set $\{1, 2, \ldots, n\}$ such that the functional value at i is a_i. In the function notation, we would write a_i as $a(i)$, and componentwise addition and multiplication of elements of S would concide with addition and multiplication of functions as defined by 3.1. Hence, if $\mathfrak{A}$ is a finite set, the complete (or discrete) direct sum of rings S_i, $i \in \mathfrak{A}$, as defined in 3.2, is essentially the same as the direct sum as defined in Chapter 1. Similar remarks hold for the case in which $\mathfrak{A}$ is a denumerably infinite set. However, we now have in 3.2 general definitions of the complete direct sum or discrete direct sum of an entirely arbitrary set of rings. Of course, for a *finite* set of rings the concept of complete direct sum coincides with that of discrete direct sum, and we shall usually in this case simply refer to the direct sum. In the finite case, we shall often continue to use the notation of n-tuples in place of the more general function notation.

In Definition 3.2, each ring S_i, $i \in \mathfrak{A}$, may be called a *component* of the complete (or discrete) direct sum of the rings S_i, $i \in \mathfrak{A}$. We may point out that it is not required that the component rings of a complete direct sum be distinct. In fact, as an important special case, they might all be identical. If $S_i = R$ for every $i \in \mathfrak{A}$, the functions which are elements of the complete direct sum of the rings S_i, $i \in \mathfrak{A}$, are then, in the usual terminology for functions, simply the functions from the set $\mathfrak{A}$ to the set R.

If S is the complete direct sum of rings S_i, $i \in \mathfrak{A}$, with each element i of $\mathfrak{A}$ we may associate a mapping θ_i of S onto S_i as follows:

3.4 $$a\theta_i = a(i), \qquad a \in S.$$

Clearly, $S\theta_i = S_i$, that is, every element of S_i is the image of some element of S. Moreover, it follows immediately from 3.1 that θ_i is a homomorphism of S onto S_i. If, now, T is a *subring* of S, $T\theta_i$ is a subring of S_i. The case in which we are most interested is that in which $T\theta_i = S_i$ for each $i \in \mathfrak{A}$. We therefore make the following definition.

3.5   Definition.   Let T be a subring of the direct sum S of rings S_i, $i \in \mathfrak{A}$, and for each $i \in \mathfrak{A}$ let θ_i be the homomorphism of S onto S_i defined by 3.4. If $T\theta_i = S_i$ for every $i \in \mathfrak{A}$, T is said to be a *subdirect sum* of the rings S_i, $i \in \mathfrak{A}$.

Let us restate this definition in another way. The subring T of the complete direct sum S of rings S_i, $i \in \mathfrak{A}$, is a subdirect sum of the rings S_i if for each $i \in \mathfrak{A}$ every element of S_i occurs at least once as the value at i of some function in T.

As a special case, the complete direct sum of rings S_i, $i \in \mathfrak{A}$, is a subdirect sum of these rings. So, also, is their discrete direct sum. However, there may be many other subdirect sums of these same rings.

If a ring R is isomorphic to a subdirect sum T of rings S_i, $i \in \mathfrak{A}$, T may be referred to as a *representation* of R as a subdirect sum of the rings S_i, $i \in \mathfrak{A}$. If α is a given isomorphism of R onto T and θ_i is the mapping 3.4, then the mapping ϕ_i defined by $r\phi_i = (r\alpha)\theta_i$ is a homomorphism of R onto S_i which we may sometimes call the *natural* homomorphism of R onto S_i.

A problem of interest is that of determining conditions under which a given ring R has a representation as a subdirect sum of a given set of rings or as a subdirect sum of some set of rings of a given type. In this connection the following theorem is frequently useful.

3.6   Theorem.   *A ring R has a representation as a subdirect sum of rings S_i, $i \in \mathfrak{A}$, if and only if for each $i \in \mathfrak{A}$ there exists a homomorphism ϕ_i of R onto S_i such that if r is an arbitrary nonzero element of R, then $r\phi_i \neq 0$ for at least one $i \in \mathfrak{A}$.*

Proof: One part is almost trivial. Suppose that R is isomorphic to a subdirect sum of rings S_i, $i \in \mathfrak{A}$, and that r is a nonzero element of R. Then under the given isomorphism the image of r must be a nonzero element of the subdirect sum. Hence, if ϕ_i is the natural homomorphism of R onto S_i, not all $r\phi_i$ can be zero.

Conversely, assume that for each $i \in \mathfrak{A}$ we have given a homomorphism ϕ_i of R onto S_i, and that if r is a nonzero element of R, then $r\phi_i \neq 0$ for at least one $i \in \mathfrak{A}$. To each element r of R let us associate the function f_r defined as follows:

3.7 $$f_r(i) = r\phi_i, \qquad\qquad i \in \mathfrak{A}.$$

Then f_r is an element of the direct sum of the rings S_i, $i \in \mathfrak{A}$. Moreover, since each ϕ_i is a homomorphism, the mapping

$$3.8 \qquad\qquad\qquad r \to f_r, \qquad\qquad\qquad r \in R,$$

is clearly a homomorphism of R into the direct sum of the rings S_i, $i \in \mathfrak{A}$. But, by our assumption and 3.7, f_r is the zero function only if $r = 0$, and the kernel of the homomorphism 3.8 is therefore zero. Hence this homomorphism is an isomorphism. There remains only to show that the image of R under the isomorphism 3.8 is actually a subdirect sum of the rings S_i, $i \in \mathfrak{A}$. However, this follows at once from 3.7 since $R\phi_i = S_i$ and therefore for each $i \in \mathfrak{A}$, we have $\{f_r(i) \mid r \in R\} = S_i$.

In an *isomorphism* the image of a nonzero element is different from zero. From Theorem 3.6 and this observation, it follows that if R is homomorphic to each ring of a family $S_i, i \in \mathfrak{A}$, with the added condition that at least one of the homomorphisms is an isomorphism, then R has a representation as a subdirect sum of the rings S_i, $i \in \mathfrak{A}$. Such a representation in which for some $i \in \mathfrak{A}$ the natural homomorphism of R onto S_i is an isomorphism may be called a *trivial* representation. If none of these natural homomorphisms is an isomorphism, we have a *nontrivial* representation.

In view of the Fundamental Theorem on Homomorphisms (2.44), if ϕ_i is a homomorphism of R onto S_i, then $S_i \cong R/K_i$, where K_i is the kernel of ϕ_i. We may therefore formulate the preceding theorem as follows in terms of ideals rather than homomorphisms.

3.9 Theorem. *A ring R has a representation as a subdirect sum of rings S_i, $i \in \mathfrak{A}$, if and only if for each $i \in \mathfrak{A}$ there exists in R a two-sided ideal K_i such that $R/K_i \cong S_i$ and, moreover, $\bigcap\limits_{i \in \mathfrak{A}} K_i = (0)$.*

We may point out that, in this formulation, a trivial representation results in case $K_i = (0)$ for at least one $i \in \mathfrak{A}$.

Although it is implicit in the above remarks, let us make the following additional observation. Suppose that we start with ideals K_i, $i \in \mathfrak{A}$, in R having zero intersection, and for each i let ϕ_i be the natural homomorphism of R onto the residue class ring R/K_i, as defined in Section 12. Then, by the method described above, we obtain a representation of R as a subdirect sum of the rings R/K_i, $i \in \mathfrak{A}$, such that in this representation the ϕ_i are also the natural homomorphisms of R onto the component rings R/K_i, as defined in this section.

The significance of the two preceding theorems is that they reduce questions about subdirect sum representations of a ring R to questions about the existence of certain homomorphisms of R or, equivalently, the existence of certain ideals in R.

14. ZORN'S LEMMA

Since we shall need to make use of it in the following section, we pause to mention briefly an important tool of frequent use in algebra as well as in other branches of mathematics.

Let $\mathfrak{M}$ denote a nonempty collection of subsets of some fixed set S. A subset $\mathfrak{C}$ of $\mathfrak{M}$ is said to be a *chain* in $\mathfrak{M}$ if for A, $B \in \mathfrak{C}$, either $A \subseteq B$ or $B \subseteq A$. By the *union of the chain* $\mathfrak{C}$ we mean the union of the subsets of S which are the elements of $\mathfrak{C}$. An element M of $\mathfrak{M}$ is naturally called a *maximal* element of $\mathfrak{M}$ if it is not properly contained in any element of $\mathfrak{M}$. The following lemma states a condition under which $\mathfrak{M}$ will have a maximal element.

3.10 Zorn's Lemma. *Let $\mathfrak{M}$ be a nonempty collection of subsets of a fixed set S. If the union of each chain in $\mathfrak{M}$ is an element of $\mathfrak{M}$, then $\mathfrak{M}$ contains one or more maximal elements.*

It can be shown that Zorn's Lemma is equivalent to what is known as the "axiom of choice." Our viewpoint is that we will here consider Zorn's Lemma itself as an axiom and henceforth use it freely.

As a simple example of the use of Zorn's Lemma, we shall prove the following result.

3.11 Theorem. *If R is a ring with unity 1, and N is an ideal in R such that $N \neq R$, then there exists in R a maximal ideal M such that $N \subseteq M$.*

Proof: First, let us recall that a maximal ideal in R means an ideal which is maximal in the set of all ideals in R other than R itself.

In the above notation, let S be the set of elements of the ring R, and let $\mathfrak{M}$ be the set of all ideals X in R such that $N \subseteq X$ and $1 \notin X$. Now $1 \notin N$ since, otherwise, we would have $N = R$. Accordingly, $N \in \mathfrak{M}$ and $\mathfrak{M}$ is therefore not empty. We now assert that the union U of an arbitrary chain $\mathfrak{C}$ in $\mathfrak{M}$ is an element of $\mathfrak{M}$. For if a, $b \in U$, then there exist elements A and B of $\mathfrak{C}$ such that $a \in A$ and $b \in B$. But, since

$\mathfrak{C}$ is a chain, we have $A \subseteq B$ or $B \subseteq A$. Suppose, for convenience of notation, that $A \subseteq B$. Then a, $b \in B$ and, since B is an ideal in R, we have $a - b \in B$. Also, $ra \in B$ and $ar \in B$ for every $r \in R$. Thus $a - b \in U$, $ra \in U$, $ar \in U$, and U is an ideal in R. By the very definition of $\mathfrak{M}$, $N \subseteq U$. Moreover, since no element of $\mathfrak{M}$ (and therefore of $\mathfrak{C}$) contains 1, we have $1 \notin U$. This shows that $U \in \mathfrak{M}$ and Zorn's Lemma states that $\mathfrak{M}$ contains a maximal element M. There remains to prove that M is actually a maximal ideal in R. Since $1 \notin M$, we have $M \neq R$. Now let Q be any ideal in R such that $M \subset Q$. Since M is maximal in $\mathfrak{M}$, $Q \notin \mathfrak{M}$. But $N \subseteq M \subset Q$, so if $1 \notin Q$, then $Q \in \mathfrak{M}$, a contradiction. Hence $1 \in Q$ and $Q = R$. Thus M is a maximal ideal in R, and the proof is completed.

15. SUBDIRECTLY IRREDUCIBLE RINGS

We now make the following definition.

3.12 Definition. A ring is said to be *subdirectly irreducible* if it has no nontrivial representation as a subdirect sum of any rings.

Clearly, a ring with only one element (the zero) is subdirectly irreducible, but this case is of little or no interest. In view of Theorem 3.9, a ring R has a nontrivial representation as a subdirect sum of rings if and only if there exists in R a set of nonzero ideals with zero intersection. Thus every representation is trivial if and only if every set of nonzero ideals has nonzero intersection or, equivalently, the set of all nonzero ideals has nonzero intersection. Hence, *a nonzero ring R is subdirectly irreducible if and only if the intersection of all nonzero (two-sided) ideals in R is different from zero.* Thus a nonzero subdirectly irreducible ring R has a unique minimal ideal $J \neq (0)$ which is contained in every nonzero ideal. In particular, every simple ring (as a special case, every field or division ring) is subdirectly irreducible.

The importance of the concept of subdirectly irreducible ring stems primarily from the following theorem.

3.13 Theorem. *Every ring R is isomorphic to a subdirect sum of subdirectly irreducible rings.*

Proof: We may obviously restrict attention to the case in which R has nonzero elements. Let a be a nonzero element of R, and consider the set of all ideals in R which do not contain the element a. This set is not empty since it contains the ideal (0). We leave it to the reader to show that Zorn's Lemma is applicable to this set and hence that it contains maximal elements. Let M_a be one such maximal element. If, then, N is an ideal in R with the property that $M_a \subset N$, it follows that $a \in N$. We now observe that the residue class ring R/M_a is subdirectly irreducible. For, by parts (ii) and (v) of Theorem 2.45 (with θ the natural homomorphism of R onto R/M_a, whose kernel is M_a) if U is a nonzero ideal in R/M_a, $U\theta^{-1}$ is an ideal in R such that $M_a \subset U\theta^{-1}$. By the remark above, $a \in U\theta^{-1}$ and hence $a\theta = a + M_a$ is an element of U and is not the zero element since $a \notin M_a$. Since every nonzero ideal in R/M_a contains the nonzero element $a + M_a$ of R/M_a, it follows that the ring R/M_a is subdirectly irreducible.

If for each nonzero element a of R we consider a corresponding ideal M_a as defined above, it follows from the fact that $a \notin M_a$ that the intersection of the set of ideals $\{M_a \mid a \in R, a \neq 0\}$ is (0). Theorem 3.9 then asserts that R is isomorphic to a subdirect sum of the rings R/M_a. Since these are subdirectly irreducible rings, the proof of the theorem is completed.

We shall find a later use for the following rather special result.

3.14   Theorem. *A subdirectly irreducible commutative ring with more than one element and with no nonzero nilpotent elements is a field.*

Proof: Let R be a subdirectly irreducible commutative ring. We first observe that if e is an idempotent in R, then e is the zero or the unity of R. For the ideals eR and $A = \{r - er \mid r \in R\}$ have zero intersection (cf. 2.18, Exercise 10) and the assumption that R is subdirectly irreducible implies that one of these ideals must be the zero ideal. If $eR = (0)$, then $e^2 = e = 0$; if $A = (0)$, then R has e as unity.

Since R is subdirectly irreducible, the intersection of all nonzero ideals in R must be different from zero. Hence there exists a nonzero element j of R which is contained in every nonzero ideal. The ideal j^2R is not the zero ideal since it contains j^3, and $j^3 \neq 0$ since R has no nonzero nilpotent elements. Hence $j \in j^2R$, that is, there is an element t of R such that $j = j^2t$. It follows that

$$(jt)^2 = j^2t^2 = (j^2t)t = jt,$$

and jt is an idempotent in R. Clearly $jt \neq 0$ since $j = j^2 t$ and $j \neq 0$. The observation made above shows that the idempotent jt must be the unity 1 of R. Moreover, every nonzero ideal in R contains j and therefore contains jt. This implies that R itself is the only nonzero ideal in R. If, then, a is a nonzero element of R, we must have $aR = R$ since $a^2 \in aR$ and $a^2 \neq 0$ since R has no nonzero nilpotent elements. Thus the equation $ax = 1$ has a solution a^{-1} in R, and R is therefore a field.

3.15 EXERCISES

1. Let $S = S_1 \oplus S_2 \oplus \cdots \oplus S_n$ be the direct sum of the finite number of rings S_i ($i = 1, 2, \ldots, n$), each with a unity, and let us denote an element a of S by an n-tuple

$$a = (a_1, a_2, \ldots, a_n), \qquad a_i \in S_i;\ i = 1, 2, \ldots, n.$$

For each i, let θ_i be the homomorphism (as in 3.4) of S onto S_i defined by: $a\theta = a_i$, $a \in S$. Prove each of the following:

(i) Let B be an ideal (right ideal) in S and let k be a fixed integer from the set $\{1, 2, \ldots, n\}$. If $b_k \in B\theta_k$, there exists an element b of B whose k^{th} component is b_k and whose other components are all zero.

(ii) If B is an ideal (right ideal) in S, then

$$B = B\theta_1 \oplus B\theta_2 \oplus \cdots \oplus B\theta_n.$$

(iii) The ideals (right ideals) in S are precisely those ideals (right ideals) of the form $A_1 \oplus A_2 \oplus \cdots \oplus A_n$, where A_i is an ideal (right ideal) in S_i ($i = 1, 2, \ldots, n$).

(iv) The d.c.c. (or a.c.c.) for right ideals holds in S if and only if it holds in each of the component rings S_i ($i = 1, 2, \ldots, n$).

2. If R is the subring of $I/(8)$ consisting of the set $\{0, 2, 4, 6\}$, verify that $\{(0, 0), (4, 4)\}$ is an ideal in $R \oplus R$. Use this example to show that the conclusions of the first three parts of the preceding exercise need not be true if the component rings do not have unities.

3. Show that the ring $I/(n)$ of integers modulo the positive integer n is subdirectly irreducible if and only if n is a power of a prime. Determine the minimal nonzero ideal in each subdirectly irreducible ring of this type.

4. Show that the ring I has a representation as a subdirect sum of fields and also has a representation as a subdirect sum of subdirectly irreducible rings none of which is a field.

5. Let a be an element of a ring R, and let A be the right ideal $\{ar - r \mid r \in R\}$ in R. If $a \notin A$, use Zorn's Lemma to show that there exists a maximal right ideal in R which does not contain the element a.

6. If R is a subdirectly irreducible ring (not necessarily commutative) with no nonzero nilpotent elements, use the result of 1.13, Exercise 23, to show that an idempotent in R is either the zero or the unity of R.

7. If R is a nonzero subdirectly irreducible ring with the property that for each element a of R there exists an integer $n > 1$ (possibly depending on a) such that $a^n = a$, prove each of the following:

(i) R contains no nonzero nilpotent elements.

(ii) a^{n-1} is idempotent.

(iii) R is a division ring.

8. Prove that if R is an arbitrary nonzero ring with the property that for each element a of R there exists an integer $n > 1$ (possibly depending on a) such that $a^n = a$, then R is isomorphic to a subdirect sum of division rings with this same property.

16. BOOLEAN RINGS

We recall that a Boolean ring is a nonzero ring in which every element is idempotent, and we know (1.13, Exercise 22) that such a ring is necessarily commutative and has characteristic 2. We now prove the following result.

3.16 Theorem. *A ring is isomorphic to a subdirect sum of fields $I/(2)$ if and only if it is a Boolean ring.*

Proof: Since both of the elements of $I/(2)$ are idempotent, it is obvious that a subdirect sum of any family of these fields is a Boolean ring. Conversely, suppose that B is a Boolean ring. Then Theorem 3.13 shows that B is isomorphic to a subdirect sum of nonzero subdirectly irreducible rings. Now each of these subdirectly irreducible rings is a homomorphic image of B and is therefore a Boolean ring. Moreover, a Boolean ring contains no nonzero nilpotent elements and Theorem 3.14 shows that a subdirectly irreducible Boolean ring is a field. The proof is completed by the observation that a field in which every element satisfies the equation $x^2 = x$ has exactly two elements and therefore is (isomorphic to) the field $I/(2)$.

We defined on page 7 what we called the ring of all subsets of a given set A. Naturally, any subring of this ring is called a ring of subsets of A. By the definition of multiplication in a ring of subsets it is apparent that such a ring is a Boolean ring. The next theorem essentially asserts that there are no other Boolean rings.

3.17 Theorem. *Every Boolean ring B is isomorphic to a ring of subsets of some set.*

Proof: If B is a Boolean ring, Theorems 3.16 and 3.6 assert that there exists some set $H = \{\phi_i \mid i \in \mathfrak{A}\}$ of homomorphisms of B onto $I/(2)$ such that if a is a nonzero element of B, then $a\phi_i \neq 0$ for some $i \in \mathfrak{A}$. We shall show that B is isomorphic to a ring of subsets of the set H.

If we denote the elements of $I/(2)$ by 0 and 1, for every $a \in B$ and every $\phi_i \in H$ we have $a\phi_i = 0$ or $a\phi_i = 1$. Let us set $H_a = \{\phi_i \mid i \in \mathfrak{A}, a\phi_i = 1\}$. Suppose, now, that $a, b \in B$ such that $H_a = H_b$. This implies that $a\phi_i = b\phi_i$, or $(a - b)\phi_i = 0$, for *every* $i \in \mathfrak{A}$. In turn, this implies that $a - b = 0$, and $a = b$. These remarks show that the mapping $a \to H_a$, $a \in B$, is a one-one mapping of B onto a certain set of subsets of H.

We next observe that since $(ab)\phi_i = (a\phi_i)(b\phi_i)$, we have $(ab)\phi_i = 1$ if and only if $a\phi_i = 1$ and $b\phi_i = 1$. This shows that $H_{ab} = H_a \cdot H_b$, since in a ring of subsets the product is defined to be the intersection. Similarly, $(a + b)\phi_i = a\phi_i + b\phi_i = 1$ if and only if one of $a\phi_i$, $b\phi_i$ is 1 and the other is zero (since $1 + 1 = 0$ in $I/(2)$). By the definition of addition in a ring of subsets, we therefore have $H_{a+b} = H_a + H_b$. These calculations show that the mapping $a \to H_a$, $a \in B$, is an isomorphism of B into the ring of all subsets of H, hence onto a subring of this ring. This completes the proof of the theorem.

17. A SPECIAL RESULT

We conclude this chapter with the following theorem for which we shall find later use.

3.18 Theorem. *If there exists in a ring R a finite number of maximal ideals M_i ($i = 1, 2, \ldots, n$) with zero intersection, then R is isomorphic to the direct sum of some or all of the simple rings R/M_i ($i = 1, 2, \ldots, n$).*

Proof: Suppose the notation is so chosen that $\{M_1, \ldots, M_k\}$ is a minimal set of the given ideals which has zero intersection. That is, $\bigcap_{i=1}^{k} M_i = (0)$, but the intersection of any $k - 1$ of these ideals is different from zero. We know, by Theorem 3.9, that R is isomorphic to a subdirect sum T of the rings R/M_i ($i = 1, 2, \ldots, k$). We shall show that this subdirect sum is actually the direct sum.

Let the known isomorphism of R onto T be given by

3.19 $$a \to (a_1, a_2, \ldots, a_k), \qquad a \in R,$$

and let us denote the natural homomorphism of R onto R/M_i by θ_i, so that $a\theta_i = a_i$. Now, by the minimal property of the set $\{M_1, \ldots, M_k\}$, there exists, for example, an element c in $\bigcap\limits_{i=2}^{k} M_i$ such that $c \notin M_1$. Then $c\theta_i = 0$ $(i = 2, \ldots, k)$, $c\theta_1 = c_1 \neq 0$; and hence under the isomorphism 3.19 of R onto T we have

$$c \rightarrow (c_1, 0, \ldots, 0)$$

with $c_1 \neq 0$. Since R/M_1 is a simple ring, $(c_1) = R/M_1$, and hence, by 2.6, an arbitrary element x_1 of R/M_1 is expressible in the form

$$x_1 = nc_1 + s_1c_1 + c_1t_1 + \sum s_{1j}c_1t_{1j},$$

where n is an integer and the other letters represent elements of R/M_1. But since θ_1 is a homomorphism of R onto the ring R/M_1, there must exist elements s, t, s_j, t_j of R such that $s\theta_1 = s_1$, $t\theta_1 = t_1$, $s_j\theta_1 = s_{1j}$, $t_j\theta_1 = t_{1j}$. Then if we set

$$x = nc + sc + ct + \sum s_j ct_j,$$

clearly $x\theta_1 = x_1$ and $x\theta_i = 0$ for $i \neq 1$. It follows that under the isomorphism 3.19 of R onto T every element of the direct sum of the rings R/M_i $(i = 1, 2, \ldots, k)$ of the form

$$(x_1, 0, \ldots, 0), \qquad\qquad x_1 \in R/M_1,$$

occurs as the image of some element of R, and hence that T contains all these elements. In like manner, T contains every element of the form

$$(0, x_2, 0, \ldots, 0), \qquad\qquad x_2 \in R/M_2,$$

and so on. Since every element $(x_1, x_2, \ldots, x_k)$ of the direct sum of the rings R/M_i $(i = 1, 2, \ldots, k)$ is a sum of such elements, we see that the subdirect sum T is actually the direct sum of the rings R/M_i $(i = 1, 2, \ldots, k)$. This completes the proof of the theorem.

At the present time we may make one application of this theorem as follows. Suppose that B is a Boolean ring with a finite number of elements. Since B has only a finite number of ideals, it follows (Theorem 3.16) that in B there exist a finite number of ideals M_i with zero intersection and such that $B/M_i \cong I/(2)$. The ideals M_i are maximal ideals since $I/(2)$ is a field (and therefore simple). Theorem 3.18 then assures us that B is isomorphic to the direct sum of a finite number of fields $I/(2)$. Suppose that $B \cong B_1 \oplus B_2 \oplus \cdots \oplus B_k$, where each B_i is $I/(2)$, and let us set $H = \{1, 2, \ldots, k\}$. For each $a \in B$, let H_a denote the set of all those integers j such that the jth component of the corresponding element of the direct sum is 1. Although the notation is now slightly different, essentially as in the proof of Theorem 3.17 it follows that the mapping $a \to H_a$, $a \in B$, is an isomorphism of B onto a ring of subsets of H. However, since we have a direct sum, *every* subset of H is clearly of the form H_a for some a in H. We have therefore proved the following result.

3.20 Theorem. *A finite Boolean ring is isomorphic to the ring of all subsets of some finite set. Such a Boolean ring therefore has 2^k elements for some positive integer k.*

3.21 EXERCISES

1. Let p be a positive prime and let us call a nonzero commutative ring R a *p-ring* if it has characteristic p and $a^p = a$ for every element a of R. Generalize Theorem 3.16 by proving that a ring is isomorphic to a subdirect sum of fields $I/(p)$ if and only if it is a *p*-ring.

2. Prove that a finite *p*-ring has p^k elements for some positive integer k.

CHAPTER 4

Prime Ideals
and the Prime Radical

A PRIME INTEGER p has the fundamental property that if a and b are integers such that ab is divisible by p, then a is divisible by p or b is divisible by p. In terms of the ideal (p) in the ring I of integers, this property may be restated as follows:

If $a, b \in I$ such that $ab \in (p)$, then $a \in (p)$ or $b \in (p)$.

The form of this statement suggests that we might define a prime *ideal P* in a ring R by the property:

4.1   If $a, b \in R$ such that $ab \in P$, then $a \in P$ or $b \in P$.

It turns out that this concept is in fact very useful in studying *commutative* rings, but is too restrictive to be of much use in the study of noncommutative rings. In the next section we shall give an appropriate definition (4.2) of a prime ideal in an arbitrary ring and prove a few properties of prime ideals. It will turn out that for commutative rings our definition of prime ideal is, in fact, equivalent to 4.1. This chapter will be devoted to an exposition of a number of results in which the concept of prime ideal plays a dominant role.

18. PRIME IDEALS AND m-SYSTEMS

We begin this section by making the following definition.

4.2 Definition.   An ideal P in a ring R is said to be a *prime ideal* if and only if it has the following property:
   If A and B are ideals in R such that $AB \subseteq P$, then $A \subseteq P$ or $B \subseteq P$.

There are several alternative, and useful, equivalent formulations of this definition. We state them as the following theorem.

4.3   Theorem.   *If P is an ideal in a ring R, all of the following conditions are equivalent:*

   (i) *P is a prime ideal.*

  (ii) *If a, b $\in$ R such that aRb $\subseteq$ P, then a $\in$ P or b $\in$ P.*

 (iii) *If (a) and (b) are principal ideals in R such that (a)(b) $\subseteq$ P, then
        a $\in$ P or b $\in$ P.*

 (iv) *If U and V are right ideals in R such that UV $\subseteq$ P, then U $\subseteq$ P
        or V $\subseteq$ P.*

  (v) *If U and V are left ideals in R such that UV $\subseteq$ P, then U $\subseteq$ P
        or V $\subseteq$ P.*

Proof: We first prove that (i) implies (ii). Let us then assume the truth of (i) and suppose that $aRb \subseteq P$. It follows that $RaRbR \subseteq P$ and hence also that $(RaR)(RbR) \subseteq P$. Since RaR and RbR are ideals, property (i) implies that $RaR \subseteq P$ or $RbR \subseteq P$. Suppose that $RaR \subseteq P$. If we set $A = (a)$, it follows that $A^3 \subseteq RaR \subseteq P$ and, again using (i), we have $A \subseteq P$ and $a \in P$. Similarly, if $RbR \subseteq P$, it follows that $b \in P$, and property (ii) is established.

Let us next assume the truth of (ii) and prove that (iii) is true. If $(a)(b) \subseteq P$, it follows easily that $aRb \subseteq (a)(b) \subseteq P$ and (ii) implies that $a \in P$ or $b \in P$. We have thus shown that property (ii) implies property (iii).

We now proceed to show that (iii) implies (iv). Suppose that U and V are right ideals in R such that $UV \subseteq P$. Let us assume that $U \nsubseteq P$, and prove that $V \subseteq P$. Suppose that $u \in U$ with $u \notin P$, and that v is an arbitrary element of V. Since $(u)(v) \subseteq UV + RUV \subseteq P$ and $u \notin P$, property (iii) implies that $v \in P$. Hence $V \subseteq P$, and (iv) is established. In a similar manner, it can be shown that (iii) implies (v).

It is trivial that either (iv) or (v) implies (i), and the proof of the theorem is therefore completed.

If P is an ideal in R, let us denote by $C(P)$ the *complement of P in R*, that is, $C(P)$ is the set of elements of R which are not elements of P. Now each of the equivalent conditions of the preceding theorem can be used to characterize a prime ideal in terms of some property of $C(P)$. In this connection, we shall find condition (ii) of Theorem 4.3 to be of special interest.

4.4   Definition.   A set M of elements of a ring R is said to be an *m-system* if and only if it has the following property:

   If $a, b \in M$, there exists $x \in R$ such that $axb \in M$.

For our purposes, the significance of this concept stems from the fact that the equivalence of Theorem 4.3(i) and (ii) asserts that *an ideal P in a ring R is a prime ideal in R if and only if C(P) is an m-system.*

It is trivial that R itself is a prime ideal in R. Clearly, $C(R) = \varnothing$, so in order for the preceding statement to be true without exception we explicitly agree that the empty set is to be considered as an m-system.

A set of elements of a ring which is closed under multiplication is often called a *multiplicative system*. It is obvious that any multiplicative system L is also an m-system; for if a, $b \in L$, then $\iota xb \in L$ for $x = a$ or $x = b$. Hence the concept of m-system is a generalization of that of multiplicative system.

We now define another concept whose significance will be indicated in the theorem to follow.

4.5   Definition.   The *prime radical* $\mathfrak{P}(A)$ *of the ideal A in a ring R* is the set consisting of those elements r of R with the property that every m-system in R which contains r meets A (that is, has nonempty intersection with A).

It is not obvious that $\mathfrak{P}(A)$ is an ideal in R, but the next theorem will show that this is the case. However, let us observe that A and $\mathfrak{P}(A)$ are contained in precisely the same prime ideals. By the definition of $\mathfrak{P}(A)$, it is clear that $A \subseteq \mathfrak{P}(A)$, so any prime ideal which contains $\mathfrak{P}(A)$ necessarily contains A. Suppose that P is a prime ideal in R such that $A \subseteq P$, and let $r \in \mathfrak{P}(A)$. If $r \notin P$, $C(P)$ would be an m-system containing r, and therefore we would have $C(P) \cap A \neq \varnothing$. However, since $A \subseteq P$, $C(P) \cap A = \varnothing$, and this contradiction shows that $r \in P$. Hence $\mathfrak{P}(A) \subseteq P$, as we wished to show.

If $r \in R$, then the set $\{r^i \mid i = 1, 2, 3, \ldots\}$ is a multiplicative system and hence also an m-system. Accordingly, the following result is an immediate consequence of Definition 4.5, and we state it here for future reference.

4.6   Lemma.   *If* $r \in \mathfrak{P}(A)$, *then there exists a positive integer n such that* $r^n \in A$.

We shall next prove the following fundamental theorem.

4.7   Theorem.   *If A is an ideal in the ring R, then* $\mathfrak{P}(A)$ *coincides with the intersection of all the prime ideals in R which contain A.*

Proof: By the remarks above, $\mathfrak{P}(A)$ is contained in every prime ideal which contains A. We shall complete the proof by showing that if $r \notin \mathfrak{P}(A)$, there exists a prime ideal P in R such that $r \notin P$ and $A \subseteq P$. Since $r \notin \mathfrak{P}(A)$, by the definition of $\mathfrak{P}(A)$ there exists an m-system M in R such that $r \in M$ and $M \cap A = \varnothing$. Now consider the set of all ideals K in R such that $A \subseteq K$ and $M \cap K = \varnothing$. This set is not empty since A is one such ideal. It may be verified that Zorn's Lemma can be applied to this set to show the existence of a maximal ideal, say P, in the set. It is clear that $r \notin P$ since $r \in M$ and $M \cap P = \varnothing$.

We shall complete the proof by showing that P is a prime ideal in R. The contrapositive form of condition (iii) of Theorem 4.3 will be convenient for this purpose. Suppose, then, that $a \notin P$ and $b \notin P$. The maximal property of P shows that the ideal $P + (a)$ contains an element m_1 of M; and, similarly, $P + (b)$ contains an element m_2 of M. Since M is an m-system, there exists an element x of R such that $m_1 x m_2 \in M$. Moreover, $m_1 x m_2$ is an element of the ideal $(P + (a))(P + (b))$. Now if $(a)(b) \subseteq P$, we would have $(P + (a))(P + (b)) \subseteq P$, and it would follow that $m_1 x m_2 \in P$. But this is impossible since $m_1 x m_2 \in M$ and $M \cap P = \varnothing$. Hence $(a)(b) \nsubseteq P$, and P is therefore a prime ideal. The proof of the theorem is therefore completed.

Let us now pause to make a few comments about the concepts introduced in this section for the special case in which R is a *commutative* ring. Under this restriction, it is easily seen that the condition 4.1 is equivalent to the condition of Theorem 4.3(iii). Accordingly, an ideal P in a commutative ring R is a prime ideal in R if and only if $C(P)$ is a multiplicative system.

Suppose that R is commutative and that $r \in R$. Let M be any m-system in R which contains r. Then there exists $x \in R$ such that $rxr = r^2x \in M$. Again applying the definition of m-system, there exists $y \in R$ such that $(r^2x)yr = r^3xy \in M$. Continuing in this way, it is clear that for each positive integer n there exists $t \in R$ such that $r^n t \in M$. Now if A is an ideal in R such that $r^n \in A$, then $r^n t \in A$ and $M \cap A \neq \varnothing$. This shows that, if $r^n \in A$, then every m-system containing r meets A, and hence that $r \in \mathfrak{P}(A)$. The following result (cf. 2.9, Exercise 5) is then a consequence of this observation and Lemma 4.6.

4.8 Theorem. *If A is an ideal in the commutative ring R, then*

$$\mathfrak{P}(A) = \{r \mid r^n \in A \text{ for some positive integer } n\}.$$

4.9 EXERCISES

1. If r is an element of a ring R, verify that $\{r^{2^n} \mid n \text{ a nonnegative integer}\}$ is an m-system in R. Hence conclude (even in a commutative ring) that an m-system need not be a multiplicative system.

2. With reference to the various conditions of Theorem 4.3, prove each of the following directly (without use of the theorem itself): (iii) implies (i), (ii) implies (i), (ii) implies (iv).

3. If A is an ideal in a ring R and $a \in R$ such that $RaR \subseteq \mathfrak{P}(A)$, prove that $a \in \mathfrak{P}(A)$.

4. Show that for each ideal A in a ring R, $\mathfrak{P}(A)$ contains every nilpotent ideal in R.

5. If A is an ideal in a ring R, prove that $\mathfrak{P}(A) = \mathfrak{P}(A^2)$.

6. Show that in a commutative ring R with unity, an ideal $P = R$ is a prime ideal if and only if R/P is an integral domain.

7. Prove, without using the theorem itself, that if condition (iii) of Theorem 4.3 holds and if $(a)(b)(c) \subseteq P$, then $a \in P$ or $b \in P$ or $c \in P$.

8. Let $R[x]$ be the ring of polynomials in an indeterminate x over the ring R. If P is a prime ideal in $R[x]$, show that $P \cap R$ is a prime ideal in R.

9. If A is an ideal in the ring R and P is a prime ideal in R, prove that $A \cap P$ is a prime ideal in the ring A.

10. If $R^2 = R$, as is certainly true if R has a unity, prove that every maximal ideal in R is a prime ideal.

11. If θ is a homomorphism of the ring R onto the ring S, with kernel K, show each of the following:

   (i) If P is a prime ideal in R which contains K, then $P\theta$ is a prime ideal in S.

  (ii) If U is a prime ideal in S, then $U\theta^{-1}$ is a prime ideal in R which contains K.

 (iii) The mapping $P \to P\theta$ defines a one-one mapping of the set of all prime ideals in R which contain K onto the set of all prime ideals in S.

19. SEMI-PRIME IDEALS

We now turn to a consideration of another concept as follows.

4.10 Definition. An ideal Q in a ring R is said to be a *semi-prime ideal* if and only if it has the following property:

If A is an ideal in R such that $A^2 \subseteq Q$, then $A \subseteq Q$.

Several simple facts are almost immediate consequences of this definition. In the first place, it is clear that *a prime ideal is semi-prime*.

Moreover, *the intersection of any set of semi-prime ideals is a semi-prime ideal.*

Although Definition 4.10 refers to the *square* of an ideal A, it follows easily by induction that if Q is a semi-prime ideal and $A^n \subseteq Q$ for an arbitrary positive integer n, then $A \subseteq Q$.

The following important result is fairly easy to prove but, for the sake of completeness, we write out a proof.

4.11   Theorem. *An ideal Q in a ring R is a semi-prime ideal in R if and only if the residue class ring R/Q contains no nonzero nilpotent ideals.*

Proof: Let θ be the natural homomorphism of R onto R/Q, with kernel Q. Suppose that Q is a semi-prime ideal in R and that U is a nilpotent ideal in R/Q, say $U^n = (0)$. Then $U^n\theta^{-1} = Q$ and (by 2.50, Exercise 7(iv)) it follows that $(U\theta^{-1})^n \subseteq U^n\theta^{-1} = Q$. Since Q is semi-prime, this implies that $U\theta^{-1} \subseteq Q$, and hence that $U = (0)$. Conversely, suppose that R/Q contains no nonzero nilpotent ideals and that A is an ideal in R such that $A^2 \subseteq Q$. Then $(A\theta)^2 = A^2\theta = (0)$; hence $A\theta = (0)$ and $A \subseteq Q$.

Although it is possible to prove results about semi-prime ideals that are analogous to all of those established for prime ideals in the preceding section, we shall present only a few that are essential for later applications. First, let us state the following theorem whose proof we omit since it can be established by very easy modifications of the proof of Theorem 4.3.

4.12   Theorem. *If Q is an ideal in a ring R, all of the following conditions are equivalent:*

(i) *Q is a semi-prime ideal.*

(ii) *If $a \in R$ such that $aRa \subseteq Q$, then $a \in Q$.*

(iii) *If (a) is a principal ideal in R such that $(a)^2 \subseteq Q$, then $a \in Q$.*

(iv) *If U is a right ideal in R such that $U^2 \subseteq Q$, then $U \subseteq Q$.*

(v) *If U is a left ideal in R such that $U^2 \subseteq Q$, then $U \subseteq Q$.*

Let us next make the following definition which is analogous to the definition of an *m*-system.

4.13.   Definition. A set N of elements of a ring R is said to be an *n-system* if and only if it has the following property:

If $a \in N$, there exists $x \in R$ such that $axa \in N$.

It is clear that an *m*-system is also an *n*-system. Also, the equivalence of conditions (i) and (ii) of Theorem 4.12 assures us that *an ideal Q in R is a semi-prime ideal if and only if C(Q) is an n-system.*

The following lemma will play a central role in the proof of the next theorem.

4.14 Lemma. *If N is an n-system in the ring R and $a \in N$, there exists an m-system M in R such that $a \in M$ and $M \subseteq N$.*

Proof: Let $M = \{a_1, a_2, a_3, \ldots\}$, where the elements of this sequence are defined inductively as follows. First, we define $a_1 = a$. Since now $a_1 \in N$, $a_1 R a_1 \cap N \neq \varnothing$, and we choose a_2 as some element of $a_1 R a_1 \cap N$. In general, if a_i has been defined, with $a_i \in N$, we choose a_{i+1} as an element of $a_i R a_i \cap N$. Thus a set M is defined such that $a \in M$ and $M \subseteq N$. To complete the proof, we only need to show that M is an *m*-system. Suppose that $a_i, a_j \in M$ and, for convenience, let us assume that $i \leq j$. Then

$$a_{j+1} \in a_j R a_j \subseteq a_i R a_j,$$

and $a_{j+1} \in M$. A similar argument takes care of the case in which $i > j$, so we conclude that M is indeed an *m*-system, and the proof is completed.

We can now easily prove the following theorem.

4.15 Theorem. *An ideal Q in a ring R is a semi-prime ideal in R if and only if $\mathfrak{P}(Q) = Q$.*

Proof: The "if" part of this theorem is an immediate consequence of Theorem 4.7 and the fact that any intersection of prime ideals is a semi-prime ideal. To prove the "only if" part, suppose that Q is a semi-prime ideal in R. Certainly, $Q \subseteq \mathfrak{P}(Q)$, so let us assume that $Q \subset \mathfrak{P}(Q)$ and seek a contradiction. Suppose that $a \in \mathfrak{P}(Q)$ with $a \notin Q$. Hence $C(Q)$ is an *n*-system and $a \in C(Q)$. By the preceding lemma, there exists an *m*-system M such that $a \in M \subseteq C(Q)$. Now $a \in \mathfrak{P}(Q)$ and, by definition of $\mathfrak{P}(Q)$, every *m*-system which contains a meets Q. But $Q \cap C(Q) = \varnothing$, and therefore $M \cap Q = \varnothing$. This gives the desired contradiction and completes the proof of the theorem.

In view of Theorem 4.7 and the fact that an intersection of prime (or semi-prime) ideals is a semi-prime ideal, we have the following immediate corollary to the preceding theorem.

4.16 Corollary. *An ideal Q in a ring R is a semi-prime ideal if and only if Q is an intersection of prime ideals in R.*

If A is an ideal in a ring R, the intersection of all the semi-prime ideals which contain A is the unique *smallest* (in the set-theory sense) *semi-prime ideal which contains A*. We may also state the following consequence of Theorems 4.7 and 4.15.

4.17 Corollary. *If A is an ideal in the ring R, then $\mathfrak{P}(A)$ is the smallest semi-prime ideal in R which contains A.*

4.18 EXERCISES

1. Prove Theorem 4.12.

2. Prove that the largest nil ideal (2.17) in a ring R is a semi-prime ideal in R.

3. If A is an ideal in the ring R, show that the set

$$\{r \mid \text{every } n\text{-system which contains } r \text{ meets } A\}$$

is the smallest semi-prime ideal in R which contains A.

4. If R_i $(i = 1, 2, \ldots, n)$ are rings with unity and $S = R_1 \oplus R_2 \oplus \cdots \oplus R_n$, prove that the semi-prime ideals in S are precisely those ideals of the form $Q_1 \oplus Q_2 \oplus \cdots \oplus Q_n$, where Q_i is a semi-prime ideal in R_i $(i = 1, 2, \ldots, n)$. (See 3.15, Exercise 1(iii).)

20. THE PRIME RADICAL OF A RING

Heretofore we have considered the prime radical of an ideal in a given ring. It will now be convenient to make the following definition.

4.19 Definition. The prime radical of the zero ideal in a ring R may be called the *prime radical of the ring R*.

Although inconsistent with our previous notation, we shall denote the prime radical of a ring R by $\mathfrak{P}(R)$ instead of by $\mathfrak{P}((0))$. The advantage of this new notation is that the ring R appears explicitly, and this will be helpful when prime radicals of different rings are being considered simultaneously.

Let us restate the definition of $\mathfrak{P}(R)$ in the following convenient form:

$$\mathfrak{P}(R) = \{r \mid r \in R, \text{every } m\text{-system in } R \text{ which contains } r \text{ also contains } 0\}.$$

For emphasis, we next state as a theorem two important characterizations of $\mathfrak{P}(R)$ which follow immediately from Theorem 4.7 and Corollary 4.17.

4.20   Theorem. *If $\mathfrak{P}(R)$ is the prime radical of the ring R, then*
  (i) $\mathfrak{P}(R)$ *coincides with the intersection of all prime ideals in R,*
  (ii) $\mathfrak{P}(R)$ *is a semi-prime ideal which is contained in every semi-prime ideal in R.*

Let us now prove the following result.

4.21   Theorem. $\mathfrak{P}(R)$ *is a nil ideal which contains every nilpotent right (or left) ideal in R.*

Proof: Lemma 4.6 (with $A = (0)$) shows at once that $\mathfrak{P}(R)$ is a nil ideal.

If A is a right (or left) ideal in R such that $A^n = (0)$, then $A^n \subseteq \mathfrak{P}(R)$ and $A \subseteq \mathfrak{P}(R)$ since $\mathfrak{P}(R)$ is a semi-prime ideal. This shows that $\mathfrak{P}(R)$ contains every nilpotent right (or left) ideal in R, and the proof is completed.

If a is a nilpotent element of a *commutative* ring, then (a) is a nilpotent ideal. We thus obtain the following corollary of the preceding theorem (cf. Theorem 4.8).

4.22   Corollary. *If R is a commutative ring, $\mathfrak{P}(R)$ is the ideal consisting of all nilpotent elements of R.*

We proceed to prove several theorems which follow fairly easily from results already established.

4.23   Theorem. *If S is an ideal in the ring R, the prime radical of the ring S is $S \cap \mathfrak{P}(R)$.*

Proof: We may emphasize that we are here concerned with the radical of S considered as a ring, not the radical of the ideal S in R. Let us denote the radical of the ring S by K, so that K is the intersection of all the prime ideals in S. However, if P is a prime ideal in R, $P \cap S$ is a prime ideal in S (cf. 4.9, Exercise 9), and hence $K \subseteq S \cap \mathfrak{P}(R)$. Conversely, if $a \in S \cap \mathfrak{P}(R)$, then every m-system in R which contains a also contains 0. In particular, every m-system in S which contains a

also contains 0. Hence $a \in K$, and $S \cap \mathfrak{P}(R) \subseteq K$. We have therefore shown that $K = S \cap \mathfrak{P}(R)$, and the proof is completed.

4.24   Theorem. *If $\mathfrak{P}(R)$ is the prime radical of the ring R, then $\mathfrak{P}(R/\mathfrak{P}(R)) = (0)$.*

Proof: Let θ be the natural homomorphism of R onto $R/\mathfrak{P}(R)$, with kernel $\mathfrak{P}(R)$, and suppose that $a \in R$ such that $a\theta \in \mathfrak{P}(R/\mathfrak{P}(R))$. Then $a\theta$ is contained in every prime ideal in the ring $R/\mathfrak{P}(R)$. If P is an arbitrary prime ideal in R, it contains the kernel of the homomorphism θ and hence, by Theorem 2.45 (iii), we have $P = (P\theta)\theta^{-1}$. But $P\theta$ is a prime ideal in $R/\mathfrak{P}(R)$ (cf. 4.9, Exercise 11), so $a\theta \in P\theta$ and $a \in (P\theta)\theta^{-1} = P$. We have shown that a is contained in every prime ideal in R, and hence that $a \in \mathfrak{P}(R)$. That is, $a\theta$ is the zero of the ring $R/\mathfrak{P}(R)$. This argument shows that $\mathfrak{P}(R/\mathfrak{P}(R)) = (0)$, and the proof is completed.

By Theorem 4.15, (0) is a semi-prime ideal in R if and only if $\mathfrak{P}(R) = (0)$. Moreover, by definition of a semi-prime ideal, (0) is a semi-prime ideal if and only if R contains no nonzero nilpotent ideal. Theorem 4.12 (iv) and (v) assure us that in the preceding sentence we can replace "ideal" by "right ideal" or by "left ideal." We therefore have the following result.

4.25   Theorem. *A ring R has zero prime radical if and only if it contains no nonzero nilpotent ideal (right ideal, left ideal).*

21. PRIME RINGS

In this section we shall be primarily concerned with the concept introduced in the following definition.

4.26   Definition. A ring R is said to be a *prime ring* if and only if the zero ideal is a prime ideal in R.

In view of the definition of a prime ideal and Theorem 4.3, we have a number of different conditions, each of which is equivalent to the condition that a ring R be a prime ring. In particular, a ring R is a prime ring if and only if either of the following conditions holds:

If A and B are ideals in R such that $AB = (0)$, then $A = (0)$ or $B = (0)$.

If $a, b \in R$ such that $aRb = (0)$ then $a = 0$ or $b = 0$.

It is easy to verify that if R is a *commutative* ring, then R is a prime ring if and only if it has no nonzero divisors of zero.

The importance of the concept of prime ring stems primarily from the following fact whose proof we leave to the reader. *If P is an ideal in the ring R, then the residue class ring R/P is a prime ring if and only if P is a prime ideal in R.*

Since the prime radical $\mathfrak{P}(R)$ of R is the intersection of all prime ideals in R, Theorem 3.9 and the preceding statement yield at once the following theorem.

4.27   Theorem.   *A ring R is isomorphic to a subdirect sum of prime rings if and only if $\mathfrak{P}(R) = (0)$.*

We pointed out above that the commutative prime rings are those without nonzero divisors of zero. Certainly, a simple ring R with $R^2 \neq (0)$ is a prime ring. In particular, every division ring is a prime ring. The next theorem will indicate one way of constructing new prime rings from given ones.

4.28   Theorem.   *If T is a ring with unity, the complete matrix ring T_n is a prime ring if and only if T is a prime ring.*

Proof: Let us first prove that if T is not prime, then T_n is not prime. If T is not a prime ring, there exist nonzero elements a and b of T such that $aTb = 0$. Using the matrix units E_{ij}, we have, for example, $aE_{11}T_n bE_{11} = 0$ with aE_{11} and bE_{11} nonzero elements of T_n. Hence T_n is not a prime ring.

Conversely, suppose that T_n is not a prime ring, and hence that there exist nonzero matrices $\sum\limits_{i,\,j=1}^{n} a_{ij}E_{ij}$ and $\sum\limits_{i,\,j=1}^{n} b_{ij}E_{ij}$ such that

$$\left(\sum_{i,\,j=1}^{n} a_{ij}E_{ij} \right) T_n \left(\sum_{i,\,j=1}^{n} b_{ij}E_{ij} \right) = (0).$$

Let $p, q, r,$ and s be fixed positive integers such that $a_{pq} \neq 0$ and $b_{rs} \neq 0$. As a special case of the preceding equation, we find that for each $x \in T$,

$$\left(\sum_{i,\,j=1}^{n} a_{ij}E_{ij} \right)(xE_{qr})\left(\sum_{k,\,l=1}^{n} b_{kl}E_{kl} \right) = \sum_{i,\,l=1}^{n} a_{iq}xb_{rl}E_{il} = 0.$$

In particular, the coefficient of E_{ps} must be zero, that is, $a_{pq}xb_{rs} = 0$. Since this is true for every x in T, we have $a_{pq}Tb_{rs} = 0$, and T is not a prime ring. The proof is therefore completed.

We conclude this section with the following result whose proof will make use of the preceding theorem.

4.29   Theorem. *If* $\mathfrak{P}(R)$ *is the prime radical of the ring* R, *then* $\mathfrak{P}(R_n) = (\mathfrak{P}(R))_n$.

Proof: Let us first consider the case in which R has a unity. It follows easily from Theorem 2.24 that $A \to A_n$ (A an ideal in R) is a one-one mapping of the set of all ideals in R onto the set of all ideals in R_n. Moreover, by 2.36, Exercise 7, $(R/A)_n \cong R_n/A_n$. Hence, by Theorem 4.28, R_n/A_n is a prime ring if and only if R/A is a prime ring. It follows that A_n is a prime ideal in R_n if and only if A is a prime ideal in R. Thus, if $\{P_i \mid i \in \mathfrak{A}\}$ is the set of all prime ideals in R, we have

$$\mathfrak{P}(R_n) = \bigcap_{i \in \mathfrak{A}} (P_i)_n = \left(\bigcap_{i \in \mathfrak{A}} P_i \right)_n = (\mathfrak{P}(R))_n.$$

If R does not have a unity, it can be imbedded in a ring S with unity by the method described in Section 2. Moreover, R is an ideal in the ring S. Theorem 4.23 (with R and S interchanged) then shows that $\mathfrak{P}(R) = R \cap \mathfrak{P}(S)$. By the case already proved, we have $\mathfrak{P}(S_n) = (\mathfrak{P}(S))_n$. Since R_n is an ideal in S_n, we can again apply Theorem 4.23 and obtain

$$\mathfrak{P}(R_n) = R_n \cap \mathfrak{P}(S_n) = R_n \cap (\mathfrak{P}(S))_n = (R \cap \mathfrak{P}(S))_n = (\mathfrak{P}(R))_n.$$

This completes the proof of the theorem.

22. THE DESCENDING CHAIN CONDITION AND THE PRIME RADICAL

In Section 8 we gave an example to show that a nil ideal need not be nilpotent. The d.c.c. for ideals does not hold in the ring of that example. In fact, the next theorem makes it clear that the d.c.c. for right ideals cannot hold in any ring in which there exists a nil ideal which is not nilpotent. After establishing this theorem, we make an application of it to the prime radical of a ring in which the d.c.c. for right ideals holds.

4.30   Theorem.   *If the d.c.c. for right ideals holds in a ring R, every nil right ideal in R is nilpotent.*

Proof: Let N be a nonzero nil right ideal in R. Since $N \supseteq N^2 \supseteq N^3 \supseteq \cdots$, the d.c.c. assures us that there must exist a positive integer n such that $N^n = N^{n+1} = N^{n+2} = \cdots$. We shall show that $N^n = (0)$. For convenience, let us set $M = N^n$ and let us assume that $M \neq (0)$ and seek a contradiction. Since $M^2 = M$, we have $M^2 \neq (0)$. Now consider the set $\mathfrak{A}$ of all right ideals A in R such that $AM \neq (0)$. This set is not empty since it contains M, and the d.c.c. assures us that there exists a right ideal B which is minimal in the set $\mathfrak{A}$ (cf. 2.29, Exercise 8). Since $BM \neq (0)$, there exists an element b of B such that $bM \neq (0)$. Now bM is a right ideal in R such that $bM \subseteq B$ and, moreover, the fact that $M^2 = M$ assures us that bM is an element of the set $\mathfrak{A}$. Since B is minimal in $\mathfrak{A}$, we must have $bM = B$. Hence, in particular, there exists an element m of M such that $bm = b$. This equation implies that $b = bm = bm^2 = bm^3 = \cdots$. However, m is nilpotent since M is a nil ideal, so $bm^k = 0$ for some positive integer k. It follows that $b = 0$ and hence that $bM = (0)$. This gives us the desired contradiction and we therefore conclude that $M = (0)$ and N is nilpotent. This completes the proof of the theorem.

Since in the presence of the d.c.c. for right ideals the concept of nil ideal coincides with that of nilpotent ideal, the following result follows immediately from Theorem 4.21.

4.31   Corollary.   *If the d.c.c. for right ideals holds in the ring R, then $\mathfrak{P}(R)$ is a nilpotent ideal which contains every nilpotent right ideal of R and every nilpotent left ideal of R.*

CHAPTER 5

Endomorphisms
and Linear Transformations

WE MAY BRIEFLY indicate the contents of the present chapter by saying that we here exploit the use of mappings, starting with endomorphisms of an abelian group and proceeding in a fairly natural way to linear transformations of a vector space over a division ring, to prove some well-known and fairly deep results in ring theory. In particular, we shall establish the Jacobson density theorem, and the Wedderburn-Artin structure theorem for rings in which the d.c.c. for right ideals holds. Other related results, as well as a few applications of these principal theorems, will also be included.

23. RINGS OF ENDOMORPHISMS

Let V be an additively written abelian group whose elements we shall denote by $x, y, z, \cdots$. Mappings of V into V will be denoted by $a, b, c, \cdots$. We are here interested in such mappings which preserve the operation of addition, that is, in endomorphisms of V according to the following definition.

5.1 Definition. A mapping $a: x \to xa$, $x \in V$, of the abelian group V into itself is called an *endomorphism* of V if for $x, y \in V$, we have

5.2 $$(x + y)a = xa + ya.$$

It follows easily from this definition, essentially as in the case of homomorphisms of rings, that if a is an endomorphism of V, then $0a = 0$ and $(-x)a = -(xa)$ for each x in V.

It is to be understood that equality of endomorphisms is the usual equality of mappings, in other words, $a = b$ for endomorphisms a and b of V means that $xa = xb$ for *every* x in V.

Let us denote by Δ the set of *all* endomorphisms of the abelian group V. We now define multiplication and addition on the set Δ as follows, where it is understood that a and b are elements of Δ:

5.3 $$x(ab) = (xa)b, \qquad\qquad x \in V,$$

5.4 $$x(a + b) = xa + xb, \qquad\qquad x \in V.$$

Of course, 5.3 is just the usual definition of multiplication of mappings of any *set* into itself, whereas 5.4 has meaning only because we already have an operation of addition defined on V. The fact that ab and $a + b$ are indeed endomorphisms of V and therefore elements of Δ follows from the following simple calculations in which x and y are arbitrary elements of V:

$$
\begin{aligned}
(x + y)(ab) &= ((x + y)a)b & \text{(by 5.3)} \\
&= (xa + ya)b & \text{(by 5.2)} \\
&= (xa)b + (ya)b & \text{(by 5.2)} \\
&= x(ab) + y(ab) & \text{(by 5.3);} \\
(x + y)(a + b) &= (x + y)a + (x + y)b & \text{(by 5.4)} \\
&= xa + ya + xb + yb & \text{(by 5.2)} \\
&= xa + xb + ya + yb & \\
&= x(a + b) + y(a + b) & \text{(by 5.4).}
\end{aligned}
$$

Now that we have addition and multiplication defined on the set Δ, we may state the following theorem.

5.5 Theorem. *With respect to the operations 5.4 and 5.3 of addition and multiplication, the set Δ of all endomorphisms of an abelian group V is a ring with unity.*

The commutative and associative laws of addition follow easily from the definition 5.4 of addition and the corresponding laws in V. The zero of Δ is the endomorphism which maps every element of V onto the zero of V, and the unity is the endomorphism $x \rightarrow x$, $x \in V$. If $a \in \Delta$, the mapping $-a$ of V into V defined by $x(-a) = -(xa)$, $x \in V$, is an endomorphism of V since we have

$$
\begin{aligned}
(x + y)(-a) &= -((x + y)a) \\
&= -(xa + ya) & \text{(by 5.2)} \\
&= -(xa) - (ya) \\
&= x(-a) + y(-a).
\end{aligned}
$$

We leave it to the reader to verify that $-a$ is, as the notation indicates, the additive inverse of a in Δ.

The associative law of multiplication holds for mappings of any set into itself, and certainly then for endomorphisms of V. Proofs of the distributive laws are required to complete the proof of the theorem, and we exhibit the calculations which establish one of them. If $x \in V$ and a, b, $c \in \Delta$, we have

$$
\begin{aligned}
x[a(b + c)] &= (xa)(b + c) && \text{(by 5.3)} \\
&= (xa)b + (xa)c && \text{(by 5.4)} \\
&= x(ab) + x(ac) && \text{(by 5.3)} \\
&= x(ab + ac) && \text{(by 5.4)}.
\end{aligned}
$$

It follows that $a(b + c) = ab + ac$. We leave the proof of the other distributive law as an exercise.

Before giving some examples, let us make one useful observation as follows. If we set $y = x$ in 5.2, we obtain $(2x)a = 2(xa)$. Then, setting $y = 2x$, we get $(3x)a = 3(xa)$. In general, if a is an endomorphism of V and m is an arbitrary integer (positive, negative, or zero), we have for each $x \in V$,

5.6 $$\qquad\qquad\qquad (mx)a = m(xa).$$

In particular, if V happens to be a cyclic group with generator z, the image of every element of V under a given endomorphism of V is determined as soon as we know the image of the generator z under this endomorphism.

EXAMPLE 1. Let V be an infinite cyclic group which we may consider to be the additive group I^+ of the ring I of integers. Corresponding to each integer k, there exists an endomorphism a_k of V defined as follows:

5.7 $$\qquad\qquad\qquad xa_k = xk, \qquad\qquad\qquad x \in I^+.$$

Of course, xk is to be interpreted as the product of x and k in the ring I. Under the endomorphism a_k, the image of the generator 1 of I^+ is k. It therefore follows by the remarks above that every endomorphism of I^+ is of the form 5.7 for some choice of k. We observe also that $a_k = a_l$ if and only if $k = l$. Hence the mapping $a_k \to k$, $k \in I$, is a one-one mapping of the ring Δ of all endomorphisms of I^+ onto the ring I.

Moreover, using 5.3, 5.4, and 5.7, it is seen that this mapping is in fact an isomorphism of the ring Δ onto the ring I. Thus the ring of all endomorphisms of the abelian group I^+ is isomorphic to the ring I.

EXAMPLE 2. Let V be the additive group of the ring $I \oplus I$, that is, V is the group whose elements are pairs (m, n) of integers with componentwise addition. Let a be an endomorphism of V and suppose that

5.8
$$(1, 0)a = (a_{11}, a_{12}),$$
$$(0, 1)a = (a_{21}, a_{22}).$$

We now observe that the image of every element (m, n) of V is determined from equations 5.8 by use of 5.6 as follows:

$$\begin{aligned} (m, n)a &= [m(1, 0) + n(0, 1)]a \\ &= [m(1, 0)]a + [n(0, 1)]a \\ &= m[(1, 0)a] + n[(0, 1)a] \\ &= m(a_{11}, a_{12}) + n(a_{21}, a_{22}). \end{aligned}$$

This calculation therefore shows that

5.9 $$(m, n)a = (ma_{11} + na_{21}, ma_{12} + na_{22}), \qquad (m, n) \in V.$$

Conversely, if we start by letting a_{11}, a_{12}, a_{21}, and a_{22} be arbitrary integers and use 5.9 to *define* a mapping a of V onto V, it is easily verified that a is an endomorphism of V and that, as a special case of 5.9, equations 5.8 hold.

Now the integers a_{11}, a_{12}, a_{21}, and a_{22} in 5.8 may be specified by giving the matrix

$$\begin{bmatrix} a_{11} & a_{12} \\ a_{21} & a_{22} \end{bmatrix},$$

and our observations above show that the mapping

$$a \to \begin{bmatrix} a_{11} & a_{12} \\ a_{21} & a_{22} \end{bmatrix}$$

is a one-one mapping of the ring Δ of all endomorphisms of V onto the complete matrix ring I_2. Actually, this mapping is an isomorphism of

Δ onto I_2. It is easy to verify that addition is preserved, so let us consider multiplication. Suppose, then, that we have

$$a \rightarrow \begin{bmatrix} a_{11} & a_{12} \\ a_{21} & a_{22} \end{bmatrix}, \qquad b \rightarrow \begin{bmatrix} b_{11} & b_{12} \\ b_{21} & b_{22} \end{bmatrix}.$$

Hence 5.8 holds, and we have also that

$$(1, 0)b = (b_{11}, b_{12}),$$

and

$$(0, 1)b = (b_{21}, b_{22}).$$

It then follows that

$$\begin{aligned} (1, 0)(ab) &= [(1, 0)a]b \\ &= (a_{11}, a_{12})b \\ &= [a_{11}(1, 0) + a_{12}(0, 1)]b \\ &= a_{11}[(1, 0)b] + a_{12}[(0, 1)b] \\ &= (a_{11}b_{11} + a_{12}b_{21}, a_{11}b_{12} + a_{12}b_{22}). \end{aligned}$$

A similar calculation will show that

$$(0, 1)(ab) = (a_{21}b_{11} + a_{22}b_{21}, a_{21}b_{12} + a_{22}b_{22}).$$

Hence we have

$$ab \rightarrow \begin{bmatrix} a_{11}b_{11} + a_{12}b_{21} & a_{11}b_{12} + a_{12}b_{22} \\ a_{21}b_{11} + a_{22}b_{21} & a_{21}b_{12} + a_{22}b_{22} \end{bmatrix} = \begin{bmatrix} a_{11} & a_{12} \\ a_{21} & a_{22} \end{bmatrix} \cdot \begin{bmatrix} b_{11} & b_{12} \\ b_{21} & b_{22} \end{bmatrix},$$

and multiplication is preserved. The ring of all endomorphisms of the additive group of the ring $I \oplus I$ is therefore isomorphic to the complete matrix ring I_2. This result will be generalized in 5.20, Exercise 3.

The theorem to follow will give a characterization of those endomorphisms of an abelian group V which have inverses in the ring of all endomorphisms of V.

5.10 Theorem. *Let Δ be the ring of all endomorphisms of an abelian group V. If $a \in \Delta$, then a has an inverse in Δ if and only if a is a one-one mapping of V onto V.*

Proof: Suppose, first, that a has an inverse b in Δ, so that $ab = ba = 1$.

Then for each $x \in V$ we have $(xb)a = x(ba) = x$, and a is clearly a mapping *onto* V. Moreover, if x_1, $x_2 \in V$ such that $x_1 a = x_2 a$, then

$$x_1 = x_1(ab) = (x_1 a)b = (x_2 a)b = x_2(ab) = x_2,$$

and this shows that the mapping is a one-one mapping.

Next, let us assume that the endomorphism a is a one-one mapping of V onto V, so that every element of V is uniquely expressible in the form xa, $x \in V$. We may therefore define a mapping b of V into V as follows:

5.11 $$(xa)b = x, \qquad\qquad x \in V.$$

Since, if x, $y \in V$,

$$(xa + ya)b = ((x + y)a)b = x + y = (xa)b + (ya)b,$$

we see that b is an endomorphism of V. Moreover, 5.11 implies that $x(ab) = x$ for every x in V, and hence that $ab = 1$. Finally, if $x \in V$, then

$$(xa)(ba) = (x(ab))a = xa.$$

This is equivalent to the statement that $y(ba) = y$ for every element y of V. Hence $ba = 1$, and b is the inverse of a in Δ.

Any ring whose elements are endomorphisms of an abelian group V is naturally called a ring of endomorphisms of V. Of course, any such ring is a subring of the ring of all endomorphisms of V.

Suppose, now, that we start with a given ring R, and let Δ be the ring of all endomorphisms of the additive group R^+ of R. If a is a fixed element of R, the mapping $x \rightarrow xa$, $x \in R$, of R into R is called the *right multiplication* by a. It will be convenient to denote this right multiplication by a_r, that is, the mapping a_r is defined by

$$xa_r = xa, \qquad\qquad x \in R.$$

One of the distributive laws in R shows that a_r is an endomorphism of R^+ and therefore $a_r \in \Delta$ for each $a \in R$. If a, $b \in R$, then $a_r + b_r$ and $a_r b_r$ are defined in Δ. Moreover, we observe that for each x in R,

$$\begin{aligned} x(a + b)_r &= x(a + b) = xa + xb \\ &= xa_r + xb_r = x(a_r + b_r), \end{aligned}$$

and

$$x(ab)_r = x(ab) = (xa)b$$
$$= (xa_r)b_r = x(a_rb_r).$$

Thus we have

5.12
$$(a + b)_r = a_r + b_r,$$
$$(ab)_r = a_rb_r.$$

Hence $a_r + b_r$ and a_rb_r are themselves right multiplications and the set Σ of all right multiplications is a subring of Δ. Moreover, the relations 5.12 show that the mapping $a \to a_r$, $a \in R$, is a homomorphism of R onto Σ. If a is in the kernel of this homomorphism, then $xa = 0$ for every element x of R. If R happens to have a unity, this implies that $a = 0$ and in this case the kernel is certainly zero, and the homomorphism is an isomorphism. We have therefore established the following result.

5.13 Lemma. *If the ring R has a unity, R is isomorphic to the ring of all its right multiplications.*

For our purposes, the importance of this lemma is that it leads almost immediately to the following result.

5.14 Theorem. *Every ring R is isomorphic to a ring of endomorphisms of some abelian group.*

The preceding lemma disposes of the case in which R has a unity. If R does not have a unity, we imbed it in a ring S with unity by the method of Section 2. Then, by Lemma 5.13, S is isomorphic to a ring of endomorphisms of S^+. Since R is a subring of S, R also is isomorphic to a ring of endomorphisms of S^+.

24. IRREDUCIBLE RINGS OF ENDOMORPHISMS

We shall continue to let V be an additively written abelian group. If R is a ring of endomorphisms of V and U is a subset of V, we naturally define UR as follows:

$$UR = \{xa \mid x \in U, a \in R\}.$$

If U consists of a single element y of V, we write yR instead of $\{y\}R$, that is, $yR = \{ya \mid a \in R\}$.

5.15 Definition. If R is a ring of endomorphisms of the abelian group V and W is a subgroup of V such that $WR \subseteq W$, then W may be called an *R-subgroup* of V.

Clearly, the zero subgroup (which we shall usually denote simply by "0") and the entire group V are always R-subgroups. We shall be particularly interested in the case in which there are no R-subgroups except these two trivial ones.

5.16 Definition. Let R be a nonzero ring of endomorphisms of the abelian group V. If the only R-subgroups W of V are $W = 0$ and $W = V$, we say that R is an *irreducible ring of endomorphisms of V*.

We may remark that if V is the zero group (having only the zero element) the only endomorphism of V is the zero endomorphism. Since in the preceding definition R is required to be a *nonzero* ring of endomorphisms of V, when we speak of an irreducible ring of endomorphisms of V it is implicit that V must have nonzero elements.

We shall next prove the following useful result.

5.17 Lemma. *If R is a nonzero ring of endomorphisms of an abelian group V, then R is an irreducible ring of endomorphisms of V if and only if $xR = V$ for every nonzero element x of V.*

Proof: One part is essentially trivial. For if $xR = V$ for every nonzero element x of V, it is clear that V is the only nonzero R-subgroup of V, and R is therefore irreducible.

Conversely, let us assume that R is an irreducible ring of endomorphisms of V and that x is an arbitrary nonzero element of V. It is easily verified that xR is a subgroup of V and since $(xR)R \subseteq xR$, it is an R-subgroup of V. It follows that $xR = 0$ or $xR = V$. Suppose that $xR = 0$, and let $[x]$ be the subgroup of V generated by x (that is, $[x] = \{nx \mid n \text{ an integer}\}$). Then $[x]R = 0$ and therefore $[x]$ is an R-subgroup of V. Since $x \in [x]$ and $x \neq 0$, we must have $[x] = V$ and therefore $VR = 0$. However, this is impossible since R has nonzero elements, and the assumption that $xR = 0$ has led to a contradiction. Hence $xR = V$, and the proof is completed.

Later on we shall have other occasions to make use of this lemma, but we now use it in the proof of the following result.

5.18   **Theorem.**   *Let R be an irreducible ring of endomorphisms of an abelian group V. If A is a nonzero ideal in R, then A also is an irreducible ring of endomorphisms of V.*

Proof: Let x be an arbitrary nonzero element of V. Since $AR \subseteq A$, we have that $(xA)R = x(AR) \subseteq xA$, so that xA is an R-subgroup of V. Since R is irreducible, it follows that $xA = 0$ or $xA = V$. Suppose that $xA = 0$. Then, using Lemma 5.17, we have $VA = (xR)A \subseteq xA = 0$, which is impossible since A is assumed to have nonzero elements. Accordingly, we must have $xA = V$. The same lemma, now applied to the ring A, shows that A is indeed an irreducible ring of endomorphisms of V, and the proof is completed.

It is often convenient to be able to speak of a ring as being isomorphic to an irreducible ring of endomorphisms of some abelian group without specifying the group. The following definition will therefore be useful.

5.19   **Definition.**   A ring which is isomorphic to an irreducible ring of endomorphisms of some abelian group may be called a *primitive ring*.

The preceding theorem then assures us that *a nonzero ideal in a primitive ring is itself a primitive ring.*

5.20   EXERCISES

1. If a, b, and c are endomorphisms of an abelian group V, prove that $(b + c)a = ba + ca$, giving the reason for each step.

2. If V is a cyclic group of order n, prove that the ring of all endomorphisms of V is isomorphic to the ring $I/(n)$ of integers modulo n.

3. Generalize Example 2 of the text as follows. Let V be the group of all n-tuples $(c_1, c_2, \ldots, c_n)$ of integers with componentwise addition, and let z_i denote the element of V whose i^{th} component is 1 and whose other components are all zero. If a is an endomorphism of V, there exist integers a_{ij} such that

$$z_i a = \sum_{j=1}^{n} a_{ij} z_j, \qquad\qquad i = 1, 2, \ldots, n.$$

Prove that the mapping $a \to (a_{ij})$ is an isomorphism of the ring of all endomorphisms of V onto the complete matrix ring I_n.

4. A one-one mapping θ of a ring S onto a ring T is called an *anti-isomorphism* if for a, $b \in S$, $(a + b)\theta = a\theta + b\theta$ and $(ab)\theta = (b\theta)(a\theta)$. If a is an element of a ring R, the mapping a_l of R into R defined by

$xa_l = ax$, $x \in R$, is called a *left multiplication*. Prove that if R has a unity, R is anti-isomorphic to the ring of all its left multiplications.

5. Prove that a division ring is a primitive ring.

6. Prove that a commutative primitive ring is a field.

7. Prove that a primitive ring is a prime ring. Give an example to show that a prime ring need not be a primitive ring.

25. R-MODULES AND RINGS OF ENDOMORPHISMS

In this section we shall introduce a concept which plays an important role in many aspects of ring theory. The definition is suggested by properties of a ring of endomorphisms of an abelian group.

5.21 Definition. Let M be an additively written abelian group and R a ring. Then M is said to be a (right) *R-module* if a law of composition of $M \times R$ into M is defined (that is, if $x \in M$, $a \in R$, xa is a uniquely determined element of M) such that the following are true for x, $y \in M$ and $a, b \in R$:

(i) $(x + y)a = xa + ya$,
(ii) $x(a + b) = xa + xb$,
(iii) $x(ab) = (xa)b$.

If R were given as a ring of endomorphisms of the abelian group M, property (i) would hold by definition of an endomorphism, and the other two properties would hold by the definitions of addition and multiplication of endomorphisms. Actually, if M is an R-module and $a \in R$, property (i) assures us that the mapping $x \rightarrow xa$, $x \in M$, is a uniquely determined endomorphism of M associated with the element a of R. However, we shall see below that R need not be (isomorphic to) a ring of endomorphisms of M simply because different elements of R may be associated with the same endomorphism of M.

Before proceeding, let us point out that if M is an R-module, each of the following is true for each $x \in M$ and each $a \in R$:

$$x0 = 0, \quad 0a = 0, \quad (-x)a = x(-a) = -(xa).$$

We leave the verification of these properties to the reader inasmuch as they are easy consequences of the defining properties of an R-module.

We have already observed that if M is an R-module and $a \in R$, then the mapping $x \to xa$, $x \in M$, of M into M is an endomorphism of the abelian group M. Let us now denote this endomorphism of M by a^*, that is, the endomorphism a^* is defined by

$$5.22 \qquad\qquad xa^* = xa, \qquad\qquad x \in M.$$

By precisely the same calculations which we used to establish 5.12 for right multiplications of a ring R we may verify that if a, $b \in R$, then the following are true:

$$5.23 \qquad\qquad \begin{aligned} (a + b)^* &= a^* + b^*, \\ (ab)^* &= a^*b^*. \end{aligned}$$

It follows easily that the set

$$5.24 \qquad\qquad R^* = \{a^* \mid a \in R\}$$

is actually a *ring* of endomorphisms of the abelian group M and that the mapping $a \to a^*$, $a \in R$, is a homomorphism of R onto R^*. It is customary to denote the kernel of this homomorphism by $(0:M)$. Thus we have

$$5.25 \qquad (0:M) = \{a \mid a \in R, xa = 0 \text{ for every } x \in M\}.$$

Clearly, by its definition, $(0:M)$ is an ideal in R and $xc = 0$ for every $x \in M$ and $c \in (0:M)$. The Fundamental Theorem on Homomorphisms (2.44) now yields immediately the following result.

5.26 Theorem. *If M is an R-module, then the ring $R/(0:M)$ is isomorphic to a ring R^* of endomorphisms of the abelian group M.*

Thus, if M is an R-module, some homomorphic image of R (R^* in the notation above) is a ring of endomorphisms of the abelian group M. In view of 5.22 and known properties of endomorphisms, we see that M may also be considered to be an R^*-module if we wish to do so.

We shall now discuss in turn two special cases that are particularly important for our purposes.

First, let us start with a ring R and let A be a right ideal in R. For the moment, let us denote by M the additive group A^+ of the ring A. For $x \in M$ (which means the same as $x \in A^+$ or $x \in A$ for that matter) and $a \in R$, we consider xa to be the product in R of the elements x and a of

R. In this case the three properties of Definition 5.21 are ring properties, so that M is clearly an R-module. It will now be convenient to denote $(0:M)$ by $(0:A)$, and hence

$$(0:A) = \{r \mid r \in R, \ Ar = (0)\}.$$

We shall now prove the following result.

5.27   Theorem.   *If A is a minimal right ideal in the ring R such that $A^2 \neq (0)$, then the ring $R/(0:A)$ is isomorphic to an irreducible ring of endomorphisms of the abelian group A^+.*

Proof: If in the present setting we let R^* be the ring defined as in 5.24 (and 5.22), the preceding theorem shows that we only need to prove that the ring R^* of endomorphisms of the abelian group A^+ is irreducible.

Since $A^2 \neq (0)$, is is clear from 5.22 that R^* must contain nonzero elements. Let a be an arbitrary nonzero element of A^+. We make use of Lemma 5.17 and complete the proof by showing that $aR^* = A^+$. In view of 5.22, this is equivalent to showing that $aR = A$. Since $a \in A$, aR is a right ideal of R which is contained in the minimal right ideal A. Accordingly, we must have either $aR = (0)$ or $aR = A$. Suppose that $aR = (0)$. Then the set $\{c \mid c \in A, \ cR = (0)\}$ is a right ideal of R contained in A; it contains the nonzero element a and hence it must coincide with A, that is, $AR = (0)$. However, this contradicts the assumption that $A^2 \neq (0)$. Accordingly, we conclude that $aR = A$, and the proof is completed.

It is easy to apply this result to establish the next theorem as follows.

5.28   Theorem.   *A prime ring which contains a minimal right ideal is a primitive ring.*

Proof: Let A be a minimal right ideal in the prime ring R. Now $A \neq (0)$ by definition of a minimal right ideal. It follows that $A^2 \neq (0)$ since R is a prime ring. Moreover, by definition of the ideal $(0:A)$ in R, we have that $A(0:A) = (0)$. Since $A \neq (0)$, we conclude that $(0:A) = (0)$, and therefore $R \cong R/(0:A)$. The preceding theorem then shows that R is a primitive ring, and this completes the proof.

We now consider another important special class of R-modules. We again start with a right ideal A in the ring R. However, we now let M be the difference group $R^+ - A^+$, as defined at the end of Section 11.

That is, M is the additive group whose elements are the cosets $x + A$, $x \in R$, with addition defined by

5.29 $$(x + A) + (y + A) = (x + y) + A, \qquad x, y \in R.$$

The zero of M is then the coset $0 + A = A$. We now define a composition of $M \times R$ into M by

5.30 $$(x + A)r = xr + A, \qquad x + A \in M, r \in R.$$

We leave it to the reader to verify that under this definition M is an R-module. Let us see what the ideal $(0:M)$ is in this case. By definition of $(0:M)$, we have

$$(0:M) = \{r \mid r \in R, (x + A)r = 0 \text{ for every } x + A \in M\}.$$

In view of Definition 5.30 and the fact that the zero of M is the coset A, this becomes

$$(0:M) = \{r \mid r \in R, Rr \subseteq A\}.$$

It is customary to denote this ideal by $(A:R)$, that is, to repeat the definition,

$$(A:R) = \{r \mid r \in R, Rr \subseteq A\}.$$

In this particular setting the ring R^* of endomorphisms of the abelian group $M = R^+ - A^+$ consists of the endomorphisms r^*, $r \in R$, defined by

5.31 $$(x + A)r^* = xr + A, \qquad x + A \in M,$$

and Theorem 5.26 assures us that $R^* \cong R/(A:R)$.

An important special case is that in which the right ideal A is a maximal right ideal. First, let us prove the following result.

5.32 Theorem. *If A is a maximal right ideal in the ring R such that $R^2 \nsubseteq A$, then the ring $R/(A:R)$ is isomorphic to an irreducible ring of endomorphisms of the abelian group $R^+ - A^+$.*

Proof: The fact that $R^2 \nsubseteq A$ assures us that $(A:R) \neq R$ and therefore that the ring $R/(A:R)$ has nonzero elements. In the notation used above,

R^* is therefore a nonzero ring of endomorphisms of the abelian group $M = R^+ - A^+$. We proceed to show that it is irreducible.

Clearly,

$$B = \{t \mid t \in R,\ tR \subseteq A\}$$

is a right ideal in R such that $A \subseteq B$. Moreover, $B \neq R$ since $R^2 \not\subseteq A$, and the maximality of A implies that $B = A$. Now let s be an arbitrary element of R which is not an element of A. Since $s \notin B$, $sR \not\subseteq A$ and, again using the maximality of A, we have $sR + A = R$. It follows from 5.31 that $(s + A)R^* = M$. The condition $s \notin A$ is equivalent to the condition that $s + A$ is not the zero element of M. Accordingly, Lemma 5.17 shows that R^* is an irreducible ring of endomorphisms of the abelian group $M = R^+ - A^+$, and the proof of the theorem is completed.

We next make the following definition.

5.33 Definition.   A right ideal A in a ring R is said to be a *modular* right ideal if there exists an element e of R such that $er - r \in A$ for every element r of R.

It is clear that if R has a unity (or just a left unity for that matter), then every right ideal in R is modular. A maximal right ideal which is also a modular right ideal will naturally be called a modular maximal right ideal. We shall now prove the following theorem.

5.34 Theorem.   *If A is a modular maximal right ideal in the ring R, then $R/(A:R)$ is a primitive ring. The ring R is itself a primitive ring if and only if it contains a modular maximal right ideal A such that $(A:R) = (0)$.*

Proof: Suppose, first, that A is a modular maximal right ideal in R. There exists an element e of R such that $er - r \in A$ for all r in R. Now $A \neq R$ since A is a maximal right ideal in R; hence, there exists $s \in R$ such that $s \notin A$. Then $es \notin A$, and this shows that $R^2 \not\subseteq A$. The first statement of the theorem then follows immediately from Theorem 5.32.

If $(A:R) = (0)$, then $R \cong R/(A:R)$, and one part of the second statement is a consequence of what we have just proved.

To prove the other part, suppose that R is an irreducible ring of endomorphisms of an abelian group V. Let x be a fixed nonzero element of V, and let us set

5.35 $A = \{a \mid a \in R, xa = 0\}.$

We shall complete the proof by showing that A is a modular maximal right ideal of R and that $(A:R) = (0)$.

Clearly, A is a right ideal in R. Since $x \neq 0$, Lemma 5.17 shows that $xR = V$ and therefore $A \neq R$. To show that A is maximal, suppose that $c \in R$, $c \notin A$, and let $B = A + (c)_r$. Since $xc \neq 0$, $xB \neq 0$. But $(xB)R \subseteq xB$, and the irreducibility of R shows that we must have $xB = V$. Therefore, for each element s of R there must exist $b \in B$ such that $xb = xs$. It follows that $x(b - s) = 0$ and $b - s \in A$. Since $A \subseteq B$, we see that $s \in B$ and therefore that $R = B = A + (c)_r$. Since this is true for every element c of R which is not in A, A is indeed a maximal right ideal in R. Now $xR = V$ implies that there exists an element e of R such that $xe = x$. Then $xer = xr$ for every element r of R, that is, $x(er - r) = 0$ and $er - r \in A$. This shows that A is modular, and there remains only to verify that $(A:R) = (0)$. If $a \in (A:R)$, then $Ra \subseteq A$ and hence $xRa = 0$. Since $xR = V$, it follows that $Va = 0$, and this implies that $a = 0$. Hence $(A:R) = (0)$, and the proof is completed.

5.36 EXERCISES

1. Prove that under the Definition 5.30, $R^+ - A^+$ is an R-module.

2. If A is a modular right ideal in the ring R, show (i) that $(A:R) \subseteq A$, and (ii) that $(A:R)$ is the largest ideal of R which is contained in A.

3. If $A \neq R$ is a right ideal in the ring R with unity, use Zorn's Lemma to prove that A is contained in a modular maximal right ideal of R.

4. Prove that a simple ring with unity is a primitive ring.

5. A one-one mapping θ of an R-module M onto an R-module N is said to be an *R-isomorphism* of M onto N if for x, $y \in M$ and $a \in R$, $(x + y)\theta = x\theta + y\theta$ and $(xa)\theta = (x\theta)a$. Suppose now that R is an irreducible ring of endomorphisms of an abelian group V, let x be a fixed nonzero element of V, and define A by 5.35. We know that V and $R^+ - A^+$ (using 5.30) may both be considered to be R-modules. Prove that the mapping θ: $(r + A)\theta = xr$, $r \in R$, is an R-isomorphism of the R-module $R^+ - A^+$ onto the R-module V.

26. IRREDUCIBLE RINGS AND VECTOR SPACES

Let R be a ring of endomorphisms of an abelian group V, and let Δ be the ring of *all* endomorphisms of V. The ring R is then a subring of Δ.

5.37 Definition. If $\alpha \in \Delta$ is such that $\alpha a = a\alpha$ for every $a \in R$, we may call α an *R-endomorphism* of V. The set D of all R-endomorphisms of V is called the *centralizer* of R in Δ.

It is easy to verify that D is closed with respect to the operations of addition and multiplication, and is actually a subring of Δ. Moreover, it certainly contains the unity of Δ. The following result will give more information about D in case R is an irreducible ring of endomorphisms of V.

5.38 Schur's Lemma. *Let R be an irreducible ring of endomorphisms of an abelian group V, and Δ the ring of all endomorphisms of V. Then the centralizer D of R in Δ is a division ring.*

Proof: Let α be an arbitrary nonzero element of D and denote by $V\alpha$ the set $\{x\alpha \mid x \in V\}$. It follows easily that $V\alpha$ is a subgroup of V. Moreover, $(V\alpha)R = (VR)\alpha \subseteq V\alpha$, and we see that $V\alpha$ is an R-subgroup of V. Now $V\alpha \neq 0$ since $\alpha \neq 0$, and the irreducibility of R shows that $V\alpha = V$. If y is a nonzero element of V, these observations, together with Lemma 5.17, establish that

$$(y\alpha)R = (yR)\alpha = V\alpha = V.$$

In particular, this shows that if $y \neq 0$ and $\alpha \neq 0$, then $y\alpha \neq 0$.

Now consider the mapping $x \to x\alpha$, $x \in V$, of V into V. Since $V\alpha = V$, this is a mapping of V onto V. Moreover, it is a one-one mapping since $x_1\alpha = x_2\alpha$ implies that $(x_1 - x_2)\alpha = 0$, and it follows that $x_1 - x_2 = 0$ or $x_1 = x_2$. Theorem 5.10 now assures us that α has a multiplicative inverse α^{-1} in the ring Δ. Actually, $\alpha^{-1} \in D$ since for $a \in R$, $a\alpha = \alpha a$ implies that $\alpha^{-1}a = a\alpha^{-1}$. We have shown that each nonzero element α of D has an inverse in D, and therefore D is a division ring.

Before discussing some of the consequences of this important result, we need to introduce the concept of a vector space over a division ring.

In the above notation and using the conclusion of Schur's Lemma we will then be able to consider V as a vector space over D. Actually, in the definition of a vector space over a field (with which we assume some familiarity), we simply replace the field by a division ring. In view of Definition 5.21 of an R-module, we may abbreviate the definition as follows.

5.39 Definition. A *vector space V over a division ring D* is a D-module with the additional requirement that if ϵ is the unity of D and $x \in V$, then $x\epsilon = x$.

If V is a vector space over a division ring D, the elements of V form an abelian group with respect to the operation of addition (ignoring the composition of $V \times D$ into V). We shall sometimes use the same symbol V for this abelian group as for the vector space, but make it clear what is meant by calling it "the abelian group V."

The requirement that $x\epsilon = x$ in Definition 5.39 of a vector space assures us that if $x \in V$ and $\alpha \in D$ such that $x\alpha = 0$, then $x = 0$ or $\alpha = 0$. For if $x\alpha = 0$ and $\alpha \neq 0$, then

$$0 = (x\alpha)\alpha^{-1} = x(\alpha\alpha^{-1}) = x\epsilon = x.$$

Except in the uninteresting case in which V is the zero vector space (that is, consists of the zero element only), it follows that if $\beta,\ \gamma \in D$ with $\beta \neq \gamma$, the mappings $x \to x\beta$, $x \in V$, and $x \to x\gamma$, $x \in V$, give distinct endomorphisms of the abelian group V. Hence D is isomorphic to a ring of endomorphisms of the abelian group V (cf. Theorem 5.26). We shall henceforth identify D with this ring of endomorphisms, that is, we shall identify $\alpha \in D$ with the endomorphism $x \to x\alpha$, $x \in V$, of the abelian group V.

Almost all of the familiar results about vector spaces over a field make no essential use of the commutativity of multiplication in the field, and they therefore hold also for vector spaces over a division ring. The reader may possibly have previously worked only with vector spaces of finite dimension. We here make no such restriction and, accordingly, we present a few brief comments about vector spaces in general.

Let V be a vector space over a division ring D. A nonempty subset U of V which is itself a vector space over D is naturally called a *subspace* of V. In view of Definition 5.15, a subspace of the vector space V

may also be described as a D-subgroup of the abelian group V. Clearly, every vector space V has as trivial subspaces V itself and the zero subspace.

The intersection of any set of subspaces of a vector space V is easily seen to be a subspace of V. If S is a set of elements of V, the intersection of all subspaces of V which contain all elements of S is called the subspace *generated by* S. We may observe that, according to this definition, the zero subspace is generated by the empty set. If S is not the empty set, it may be verified that the subspace of V generated by S is the set of all elements x of V which can be expressed as a linear combination of a finite number of elements of S, that is, in the form

$$x = y_1\beta_1 + y_2\beta_2 + \cdots + y_k\beta_k,$$

where the y's are elements of S, the β's are elements of D, and k is a positive integer.

An operation of addition may be defined on the set of all subspaces of V in the following natural way. If U_1 and U_2 are subspaces of V, we define

$$U_1 + U_2 = \{u_1 + u_2 \mid u_1 \in U_1, u_2 \in U_2\}.$$

It is easy to verify that $U_1 + U_2$ is then a subspace of V. In fact, it is the subspace generated by the set $U_1 \cup U_2$. The sum of any finite number of subspaces may be defined in the obvious way.

If $x \in V$, it is convenient to denote by xD the subspace of V generated by the set $\{x\}$, and it follows that $xD = \{x\alpha \mid \alpha \in D\}$. The subspace of V generated by the finite set $\{x_1, x_2 \ldots, x_n\}$ is the sum of the subspaces x_iD, that is, it is

$$x_1D + x_2D + \cdots + x_nD.$$

The finite set $\{x_1, x_2, \ldots, x_n\}$ of elements of V is said to be a *linearly independent set* if

$$x_1\alpha_1 + x_2\alpha_2 + \cdots + x_n\alpha_n = 0, \qquad\qquad \alpha_i \in D,$$

implies that all $\alpha_i = 0$; otherwise it is a *linearly dependent set*. An arbitrary nonempty set of elements of V is said to be a linearly independent set if each finite subset is linearly independent. A set B of elements of V is called a *basis* of V if it is a linearly independent set and V is generated by B. It is easy to verify that every element of V is *uniquely* expressible as a linear combination of a finite set of elements of a basis.

In order to avoid having to make separate statements about trivial special cases, it is convenient to consider that the empty set of vectors is linearly independent and hence that the empty set is a basis of the zero vector space.

Let us now sketch a proof that every vector space V over a division ring D necessarily has a basis. Actually, we shall prove somewhat more as follows.

5.40 Theorem. *If A is a linearly independent subset of the vector space V, then there exists a basis of V which contains the set A.*

Proof: Consider the set $\mathfrak{M}$ of all linearly independent subsets of V which contain the given linearly independent set A. The set $\mathfrak{M}$ is not empty since it contains A. We wish to apply Zorn's Lemma (3.10), so we consider the union U of the elements of a chain of elements of $\mathfrak{M}$. If $\{x_1, x_2, \ldots, x_n\} \subseteq U$, then $\{x_1, x_2, \ldots, x_n\}$ is contained in some *one* of the elements of the chain (why?), and therefore U is an independent set which contains A, so we conclude that $U \in \mathfrak{M}$. Zorn's Lemma then asserts that there exists a maximal element B of $\mathfrak{M}$, and we verify that B is a basis of V. If $x \in B$, it is trivial that x is expressible as a linear combination of elements of B. If $x \in V$, $x \notin B$, the maximal property of B shows that the set $B \cup \{x\}$ must be a linearly dependent set. That is, for certain elements $x_1, \ldots, x_n$ of B, we must have

$$x_1\alpha_1 + \cdots + x_n\alpha_n + x\alpha = 0,$$

without all of α, α_i $(i = 1, \ldots, n)$ being zero. Clearly, $\alpha \neq 0$ since the set $\{x_1, x_2, \ldots, x_n\}$, being contained in B, is linearly independent. We can therefore solve the preceding equation for x and express x as a linear combination of the elements $x_1, \ldots, x_n$ of B. This completes the proof that B is a basis of V.

If V has a basis consisting of a finite number n of elements, it can be proved that every basis of V has n elements, and we say that V has *dimension n*. The zero vector space naturally has *dimension zero*. If the nonzero vector space V does not have dimension n for any positive integer n, we say that V has *infinite dimension*.

We next make the following definition.

5.41 Definition. Let V be a vector space over a division ring D.

A mapping a of V into V is called a *linear transformation* of V if it has the following two properties:

$$(x + y)a = xa + ya, \qquad\qquad x, y \in V,$$
$$(x\alpha)a = (xa)\alpha, \qquad\qquad x \in V,\ \alpha \in D.$$

Of course, this definition takes the form of the familiar definition of a linear transformation of a vector space over a field. Before proceeding, let us point out an alternate formulation of this definition.

The first property of Definition 5.41 merely asserts that a is an endomorphism of the abelian group V. The second property asserts that $a\alpha = \alpha a$ and hence (by Definition 5.37 with D now playing the role of R) that a is a D-endomorphism of V. A linear transformation of a vector space V over a division ring D is therefore just a D-endomorphism of the abelian group V, and the set of all linear transformations of V is the centralizer of D in the ring of all endomorphisms of the abelian group V. It follows (cf. the remark following Definition 5.37) that the set of all linear transformations of V is a ring with unity.

Associated with a linear transformation a of a vector space V are two important subspaces of V as follows. The set

$$Va = \{xa \mid x \in V\}$$

is a subspace of V called the *image space* of a. Moreover, the *rank* of a is defined to be the dimension of the image space of a. The set

$$V_a = \{x \mid x \in V,\ xa = 0\}$$

is a subspace of V called the *null space* of a.

The following observations are frequently useful. Let B be a basis of the vector space V over D, so that each element x of V is uniquely expressible as a finite sum

$$x = \sum z_i\alpha_i, \qquad\qquad \alpha_i \in D,$$

where the z_i are distinct elements of B. Now if a is a linear transformation of V, it follows from the defining properties of a linear transformation that

5.42 $$xa = \sum (z_i a)\alpha_i.$$

That is, xa is determined by the images za of the elements z of a basis. In other words, *a linear transformation is completely determined by its effect upon a basis of V*. Now let us change our approach and suppose that we start with an arbitrary mapping a of a basis of V into V, so that za is given for each element z of the basis B. For each $x = \sum z_i \alpha_i$ in V, we now *define xa* by 5.42. Then a becomes a mapping of V into V, and we leave it to the reader to verify that the mapping a so defined is a linear transformation of V. We have thus shown that *a given mapping of a basis of V into V can be extended (uniquely) to a linear transformation of V*.

For our present purposes the importance of the concepts introduced in this section stems from the following observations. Let R be given as an irreducible ring of endomorphisms of an abelian group V. Then, by Schur's Lemma, the centralizer of R in the ring of all endomorphisms of V is a division ring D, and V may then be considered as a vector space over D. Since, by the definition of centralizer, every element of R commutes with every element of D, the second condition of Definition 5.41 is satisfied for $a \in R$, $\alpha \in D$, and we see that each element of R is a linear transformation of the vector space V over D. Hence R is a ring of linear transformations of the vector space V over D. This viewpoint will be exploited in the following section.

27. DENSE RINGS OF LINEAR TRANSFORMATIONS

For the present, let R be an arbitrary ring of linear transformations of a vector space V over a division ring D.

5.43 Definition.   Let k be a positive integer. Then the ring R of linear transformations is said to be *k-fold transitive* if given any ordered set $x_1, x_2, \ldots, x_k$ of k linearly independent vectors and any ordered set $y_1, y_2, \ldots, y_k$ of k arbitrary vectors, there exists $a \in R$ such that $x_i a = y_i$ $(i = 1, 2, \ldots, k)$. If R is k-fold transitive for every positive integer k, R is said to be a *dense* ring of linear transformations.

We may point out that if V has finite dimension n, any ring of linear transformations of V is trivially k-fold transitive for $k > n$ since in this case there exists no set of k linearly independent vectors in V.

Let us now give some examples of dense rings of linear transformations.

EXAMPLE 1.   Let V be an arbitrary vector space over a division ring, and let S be the ring of *all* linear transformations of V. We assert that S is then a dense ring of linear transformations of V. To see this, let k be an arbitrary positive integer, let $x_1, x_2, \ldots, x_k$ be linearly independent elements of V and $y_1, y_2, \ldots, y_k$ arbitrary elements of V. By Theorem 5.40, there exists a basis B of V which contains the set $\{x_1, x_2, \ldots, x_k\}$. We now define a mapping a of B into V as follows: $x_i a = y_i$ ($i = 1, 2, \ldots, k$), $za = 0$ for every element z of B other than $x_1, x_2, \ldots, x_k$. As described in the preceding section, we can extend a to a linear transformation of V. Since $x_i a = y_i$ ($i = 1, 2, \ldots, k$), we see that S is k-fold transitive for every positive integer k, and hence that S is dense.

Incidentally, the linear transformation a described above has finite rank since the image space Va is generated by the finite set $\{y_1, y_2, \ldots, y_k\}$. That is,

$$Va = y_1 D + y_2 D + \cdots + y_k D,$$

and the rank of a cannot exceed k.

EXAMPLE 2.   Let T be the set of all linear transformations of *finite rank* of a vector space V over a division ring D. It is not difficult to show that T is closed under addition and multiplication and is in fact a ring. It is, of course, a subring of the ring S of all linear transformations of V. Moreover, if V has infinite dimension, T is a proper subring of S since T cannot contain the unity of S. The ring T is itself a dense ring of linear transformations of V since the linear transformation a constructed in the preceding example is actually an element of T. Incidentally, T is an ideal in S (cf. 5.62, Exercise 2).

EXAMPLE 3.   Let V be a vector space with a denumerably infinite basis whose elements are ordered in a sequence $z_1, z_2, z_3, \cdots$. Let K_m be the set of all linear transformations of V which map the subspace $z_1 D + z_2 D + \cdots + z_m D$ into itself and map all of the basis elements z_{m+1}, $z_{m+2}, \ldots$ into zero. Then K_m is a ring of linear transformations of V and if $m_1 < m_2$, we have $K_{m_1} \subset K_{m_2}$. It is easy to verify that the union K of all K_m ($m = 1, 2, 3, \ldots$) is also a ring of linear transformations of V. To show that K is dense, let $x_1, x_2, \ldots, x_k$ be linearly independent elements of V and $y_1, y_2, \ldots, y_k$ arbitrary elements of V. Then all these x's and y's are linear combinations of $z_1, z_2, \ldots, z_p$ for some positive integer p (why?). Hence the linear transformation a, defined as in

Example 1, is an element of K_p and therefore also an element of K. This shows that K is a dense ring of linear transformations of V.

The next theorem, which is due to Jacobson, is of great importance in the study of the structure of rings.

5.44 Density Theorem. *Let R be an irreducible ring of endomorphisms of an abelian group V, and let D be the centralizer of R in the ring of all endomorphisms of V. Then R is a dense ring of linear transformations of V considered as a vector space over D.*

A principal part of the proof of this theorem will be disposed of by the following lemma which we proceed to establish.

5.45 Lemma. *If W is a subspace of V of finite dimension and x is an element of V such that $x \notin W$, then there exists $a \in R$ such that $Wa = 0$, $xa \neq 0$.*

The statement of the lemma is obviously true (by Lemma 5.17) for the case in which W is of dimension zero, that is, $W = 0$. The proof is by induction on the dimension of W, so let us assume that W has dimension $n \geq 1$ and that the statement of the lemma is true for every subspace of V of dimension $n - 1$. Thus we have $W = U + yD$, where U is a subspace of V of dimension $n - 1$ and $y \notin U$. Let us set

$$J = \{a \mid a \in R, \ Ua = 0\}.$$

Then J is a right ideal in R. By the induction hypothesis, there is an element b of R such that $Ub = 0$ and $yb \neq 0$; hence $yJ \neq 0$. By Lemma 5.17, $(yJ)R = V$ and since $JR \subseteq J$, we have $yJ = V$. Let x be an element of V such that $x \notin W$. We now *assume* that every element of R which annihilates W also annihilates x (that is, if $r \in R$ such that $Wr = 0$, then also $xr = 0$), and complete the proof by obtaining a contradiction. Let us tentatively define a mapping α of V (since $yJ = V$) into V as follows

5.46 $$(yj)\alpha = xj, \qquad\qquad j \in J,$$

and proceed to show that α is in fact an R-endomorphism of V. First, the mapping α is well-defined. For if $j_1, j_2 \in J$ such that $yj_1 = yj_2$, then $y(j_1 - j_2) = 0$. Since, by definition of J, we have $U(j_1 - j_2) = 0$, it follows that $W(j_1 - j_2) = 0$ and the assumption made above assures us that $x(j_1 - j_2) = 0$, that is, that $xj_1 = xj_2$. Now that α is a well-defined mapping of V into V, the following simple calculation shows that it is an endomorphism of V:

$$(yj_1 + yj_2)\alpha = (y(j_1 + j_2))\alpha = x(j_1 + j_2)$$
$$= xj_1 + xj_2 = (yj_1)\alpha + (yj_2)\alpha.$$

Finally, using 5.46 and the fact that J is a right ideal in R, we find that if $r \in R$ and $j \in J$

$$(yj)(r\alpha) = (y(jr))\alpha = x(jr) = (xj)r = ((yj)\alpha)r = (yj)(\alpha r).$$

Since $yJ = V$, this shows that $z(r\alpha) = z(\alpha r)$ for every $z \in V$, and hence that $r\alpha = \alpha r$. We have thus proved that α, defined by 5.46, is an R-endomorphism of V and therefore an element of the division ring D. Since, in particular, α commutes with elements of J, it follows from 5.46 that $(y\alpha - x)J = 0$. Now if $y\alpha - x \notin U$, the induction hypothesis would show that there exists an element of J which does not annihilate $y\alpha - x$. Hence we must have $y\alpha - x \in U$ from which it follows that $x \in W$, and this gives the desired contradiction since $x \notin W$. This completes the proof of the lemma.

The proof of the theorem now follows easily by induction. First, 1-fold transitivity of R is an immediate consequence of Lemma 5.17. Let us assume as induction hypothesis that R is $(k - 1)$-fold transitive and prove that it is k-fold transitive. Accordingly, let $x_1, x_2, \ldots, x_k$ be linearly independent elements of V and $y_1, y_2, \ldots, y_k$ arbitrary elements of V. By $(k - 1)$-fold transitivity, there exists $a \in R$ such that $x_i a = y_i$ $(i = 1, 2, \ldots, k - 1)$. By the lemma proved above, there exists $b \in R$ such that $x_i b = 0$ $(i = 1, 2, \ldots, k - 1)$, $x_k b \neq 0$. Then $(x_k b)R = V$ and there exists $c \in R$ such that $(x_k b)c = x_k(bc) = y_k - x_k a$. It follows that $x_i(a + bc) = y_i$ $(i = 1, 2, \ldots, k)$, and this shows that R is k-fold transitive. By induction we have shown that R is a dense ring of linear transformations of V, and the proof of the theorem is completed.

A dense ring of linear transformations of a vector space V is certainly an irreducible ring of endomorphisms of V considered as an abelian group. As a matter of fact, 1-fold transitivity is sufficient to assure irreducibility. It may be worth emphasizing at this point that Theorems 5.34 and 5.44 show the equivalence of the following three statements:

(i) The ring R is a primitive ring (that is, it is isomorphic to an irreducible ring of endomorphisms of some abelian group).

(ii) The ring R contains a modular maximal right ideal A such that $(A:R) = (0)$.

(iii) The ring R is isomorphic to a dense ring of linear transformations of a nonzero vector space over a division ring.

The next theorem will show that 2-fold transitivity of a ring of linear transformations actually implies that the ring is dense.

5.47   Theorem.   *If R is a 2-fold transitive ring of linear transformations of a nonzero vector space V over a division ring D, then D is the centralizer of R in the ring Δ of all endomorphisms of the group V, and R is a dense ring of linear transformations of the vector space V over D.*

Clearly, 2-fold transitivity of R implies that R is an irreducible ring of endomorphisms of V, so the desired result will follow from the preceding theorem as soon as we have proved that D is the centralizer of R in Δ. Since the centralizer of R in Δ contains D, it is enough to prove inclusion the other way.

Let k be an arbitrary element of the centralizer of R in Δ; hence k is an endomorphism of V such that $ak = ka$ for every $a \in R$. Let x be a nonzero element of V and let us assume that x and xk are linearly independent. Then, by the 2-fold transitivity of R, there exists $b \in R$ such that $xb = 0$ and $(xk)b \neq 0$. But this is impossible since $bk = kb$ and therefore $(xb)k = (xk)b$. Therefore, we know that x and xk are linearly dependent and since $x \neq 0$, it follows that $xk = x\beta_x$, $\beta_x \in D$. Similarly, if y is a nonzero element of V, there exists $\beta_y \in D$ such that $yk = y\beta_y$. Moreover, there exists $c \in R$ such that $xc = y$, and we now have

$$
\begin{aligned}
y\beta_y = yk = (xc)k = x(ck) = x(kc) &= (xk)c \\
&= (x\beta_x)c = (xc)\beta_x = y\beta_x,
\end{aligned}
$$

from which it follows that $\beta_x = \beta_y$. This argument shows that there exists an element β of D such that $zk = z\beta$ for every $z \in V$. Hence $k = \beta$, and the proof is completed.

28. SUBSPACES AND THE DESCENDING CHAIN CONDITION

Let R be a dense ring of linear transformations of a nonzero vector space V over a division ring D. If W is a subspace of V, let us define

5.48 $W^* = \{a \mid a \in R, \, Wa = 0\}.$

Then W^* is a right ideal in R which we may call the *annihilating right ideal of the subspace* W. Clearly, $V^* = (0)$, and if W_1 and W_2 are subspaces such that $W_1 \subseteq W_2$, then $W_1^* \supseteq W_2^*$. Moreover, the annihilating right ideal of the zero subspace is R. We may also point out that the proof of Theorem 5.34 shows that if W is a subspace of V of dimension one, then W^* is a modular maximal right ideal in R.

Similarly, if A is a right ideal in R, let us define

5.49 $$A^* = \{x \mid x \in V, xA = 0\}.$$

Then A^* is a subspace of V which we may call the *annihilating subspace of the right ideal* A. As special cases, it is clear that $(0)^* = V$ and that $R^* = 0$. Moreover, if A_1 and A_2 are right ideals in R such that $A_1 \subseteq A_2$, then $A_1^* \supseteq A_2^*$.

If W is a subspace of V, let us write W^{**} for $(W^*)^*$. Then W^{**} is a subspace of V and clearly we always have $W \subseteq W^{**}$. Lemma 5.45 shows that if W is a finite-dimensional subspace of V and x is an element of V such that $x \notin W$, then $x \notin W^{**}$. The following result is therefore essentially a restatement of Lemma 5.45 using the present notation.

5.50 Lemma. *If W is a finite-dimensional subspace of V, then $W = W^{**}$.*

We may remark that this lemma shows that every finite-dimensional subspace of V is the annihilating subspace of some right ideal in R.

Suppose, now, that the d.c.c. for right ideals holds in the dense ring of linear transformations of the vector space V. We assert that V must then have *finite* dimension for, otherwise, there would be an infinite ascending chain

$$W_1 \subset W_2 \subset W_3 \subset \cdots$$

of finite-dimensional subspaces of V. Then we would have

$$W_1^* \supseteq W_2^* \supseteq W_3^* \supseteq \cdots,$$

where these are right ideals in R. The preceding lemma shows that, for example, we cannot have $W_1^* = W_2^*$ since this would imply that $W_1 = W_1^{**} = W_2^{**} = W_2$, whereas $W_1 \subset W_2$. Thus we would have an infinite decreasing chain

$$W_1^* \supset W_2^* \supset W_3^* \supset \cdots$$

of right ideals in R, which violates our assumption that the d.c.c. for right ideals holds in R. This shows that V indeed has finite dimension and therefore has a finite basis $\{x_1, x_2, \ldots, x_n\}$. Since R is dense, there exists in R a linear transformation which maps these basis elements into arbitrary elements of V. Hence, in this case, R consists of the ring of *all* linear transformations of V. These results will be incorporated in the statement of the next theorem, but first we need to emphasize another definition previously mentioned in 5.20, Exercise 4.

5.51   Definition.   A one-one mapping θ of a ring S onto a ring T is called an *anti-isomorphism* of S onto T if for a, $b \in S$,

$$(a + b)\theta = a\theta + b\theta, \quad (ab)\theta = (b\theta)(a\theta).$$

Moreover, S is said to be *anti-isomorphic* to T if there exists an anti-isomorphism of S onto T.

Thus, in an anti-isomorphism sums are preserved and products are reversed. It is easy to construct a ring which is anti-isomorphic to a given ring. The case in which we are now interested is that of a division ring, so we restrict our statements to this case and at the same time introduce a notation to be used below. Let D be a division ring and let D' be the set of all symbols α', $\alpha \in D$. On the set D' we now define addition and multiplication as follows:

$$\alpha' + \beta' = (\alpha + \beta)', \quad \alpha'\beta' = (\beta\alpha)'.$$

It is trivial to verify that under these definitions D' is a division ring which is anti-isomorphic to D under the mapping $\alpha \to \alpha'$, $\alpha \in D$.

We are now ready to state the following important theorem.

5.52   Theorem.   *Let R be a dense ring of linear transformations of a nonzero vector space V over a division ring D, and suppose that the d.c.c. for right ideals holds in R. Then V is of finite dimension n over D, and R consists of all linear transformations of V. Moreover, R is isomorphic to the ring D'_n of all matrices of order n over a division ring D' which is anti-isomorphic to D.*

We have already established all but the last sentence of this theorem. Suppose that V has a basis $\{x_1, x_2, \ldots, x_n\}$. If $a \in R$ is a linear transformation of V, under the mapping a each of these basis elements must map into a uniquely determined linear combination of these basis elements. That is, there exist elements α_{ij} of D, uniquely determined by the linear transformation a, such that

$$5.53 \qquad\qquad x_i a = \sum_{j=1}^{n} x_j \alpha_{ij}, \qquad\qquad (i = 1, 2, \ldots, n).$$

We now consider the mapping

$$5.54 \qquad\qquad a \to (\alpha'_{ij}), \qquad\qquad a \in R,$$

of R into D'_n. This is a mapping of R *onto* D'_n since there exists a linear transformation of V which maps the basis elements into arbitrary elements of V, and R consists of all linear transformations of V. Moreover, it is a one-one mapping because a linear transformation is completely determined by its effect upon a basis of V. The proof will be completed by showing that addition and multiplication are preserved under the mapping 5.54 and hence that it is an isomorphism.

Suppose that a, $b \in R$ and that $a \to (\alpha'_{ij})$ and $b \to (\beta'_{ij})$. Thus 5.53 holds, and also

$$x_i b = \sum_{j=1}^{n} x_j \beta_{ij}, \qquad\qquad (i = 1, 2, \ldots, n).$$

It follows that

$$x_i(a + b) = x_i a + x_i b$$
$$= \sum_{j=1}^{n} x_j[\alpha_{ij} + \beta_{ij}], \qquad (i = 1, 2, \ldots, n),$$

so that

$$a + b \to (\,[\alpha_{ij} + \beta_{ij}]') = (\alpha'_{ij} + \beta'_{ij}) = (\alpha'_{ij}) + (\beta'_{ij}).$$

Also,

$$x_i(ab) = (x_i a)b = \left[\sum_{k=1}^{n} x_k \alpha_{ik} \right] b$$
$$= \sum_{k=1}^{n} (x_k b)\alpha_{ik} = \sum_{k=1}^{n} \left[\sum_{j=1}^{n} x_j \beta_{kj} \right] \alpha_{ik}$$
$$= \sum_{j=1}^{n} x_j \left[\sum_{k=1}^{n} \beta_{kj} \alpha_{ik} \right], \qquad\qquad (i = 1, 2, \ldots, n).$$

Thus we have under the mapping 5.54,

$$ab \rightarrow \left(\left[\sum_{k=1}^{n} \beta_{kj}\alpha_{ik} \right]' \right) = \left(\sum_{k=1}^{n} \alpha'_{ik}\beta'_{kj} \right) = (\alpha'_{ij})(\beta'_{ij}).$$

We have now shown that the mapping 5.54 is an isomorphism, and the proof of the theorem is completed.

We may remark that in the special case in which D is a *field*, so that multiplication is commutative in D, the field D' is actually isomorphic to D so there would be no point in introducing D' at all. In this case the above calculations would coincide with those, probably familiar to the reader, which are usually used to obtain a matrix representation of linear transformations of a vector space over a field.

Let us also observe that the isomorphism 5.54 of R onto D'_n depends upon the particular basis $\{x_1, x_2, \ldots, x_n\}$ of V which is used, and a change in the basis elements (or even in their order) would lead to a different isomorphism. However, we shall not here discuss the matter any further since for our present purposes the existence of one such isomorphism is all that is essential.

The following corollary will be useful a little later, so we pause to establish it before proceeding.

5.55 Corollary. *If the d.c.c. for right ideals holds in the ring R and $P \neq R$ is a prime ideal in R, then P is a maximal ideal in R and R/P is isomorphic to a complete matrix ring over a division ring.*

Proof: The ring R/P is a prime ring and the d.c.c. for right ideals holds also in R/P since it is a homomorphic image of R (2.50, Exercise 8). It follows that R/P has minimal right ideals and Theorem 5.28 shows that R/P is therefore a primitive ring. Then the Density Theorem (5.44) and Theorem 5.52 show that R/P is isomorphic to a complete matrix ring over a division ring. Such a ring is simple (2.28), and therefore P is a maximal ideal (2.46).

29. SOME PROPERTIES OF A RING D$_n$

Let us reverse the point of view of the preceding section and now *start* with a complete matrix ring D_n over an arbitrary division ring D. We first observe that D_n is isomorphic to the ring of all linear transformations of a suitable vector space. To see this, we only need to consider a vector space V of dimension n over the division ring D' which is anti-isomorphic to D, and reverse the roles of D and D' in the preceding section.

In 2.29, Exercise 4, it was shown that D_n is expressible as a direct sum of n minimal right ideals. The following result will therefore be applicable to the ring D_n.

5.56   Lemma. *Let R be a ring with unity 1 such that R is expressible as a direct sum of a finite number of minimal right ideals. Then*
   (i) *Every right ideal A in R is a direct summand, that is, there exists a right ideal B in R such that $R = A \oplus B$.*
   (ii) *Every right ideal A in R contains an idempotent e such that $A = eR$.*

Proof: By hypothesis,

$$R = M_1 \oplus M_2 \oplus \cdots \oplus M_k,$$

where the M_i are minimal right ideals in R. Let A be a right ideal in R, and we assume that $A \neq (0)$ and $A \neq R$ since these cases are trivial. Since $A \cap M_i \subseteq M_i$ and M_i is a minimal right ideal in R, we have that for each i, either $A \cap M_i = (0)$ or $M_i \subseteq A$. Clearly, $A = R$ if and only if $M_i \subseteq A$ $(i = 1, 2, \ldots, k)$. If, then, A is a proper right ideal in R, some $M_i \nsubseteq A$. Suppose the notation is so chosen that $M_1 \nsubseteq A$. Then $A \cap M_1 = (0)$, the sum $A_1 = A + M_1$ is a direct sum, and $A \subset A_1$. If $A_1 \neq R$, there exists some M_i, say M_2, such that $A_1 \cap M_2 = (0)$ and $A \subset A_2 = A_1 \oplus M_2 = A \oplus M_1 \oplus M_2$. By continuing this process we must eventually come to a right ideal, say A_q, which contains all M_i and therefore coincides with R. That is, there exists a right ideal B, actually a direct sum of certain of the M_i, such that $R = A \oplus B$. This establishes part (i) of the lemma.

Let us now prove the second part. If A is a right ideal in R, we know that there exists a right ideal B in R such that $R = A \oplus B$. In particular, $1 = e + f$, where $e \in A, f \in B$. It follows that $e = e^2 + fe$ or $e - e^2 = fe$. But $e - e^2 \in A, fe \in B$, and $A \cap B = (0)$; so $fe = 0$, $e^2 = e$, and e is an idempotent. Similarly, $ef = 0$ and $f^2 = f$. If $a \in A$, then $a = (e + f)a = ea + fa$ and, again using the fact that $A \cap B = (0)$, we see that $a = ea$ and $fa = 0$. This shows that $A \subseteq eR$ and, since $e \in A$, we have $eR \subseteq A$. Therefore, $A = eR$ and the proof is completed.

Now let R (which is isomorphic to D_n) be the ring of all linear transformations of a vector space V of dimension n over the division ring D'. If A is a right ideal in R, we have previously defined

$$A^* = \{x \mid x \in V, \, xA = 0\}$$

to be the annihilating subspace of the right ideal A. We shall now prove the following lemma, in which $(A^*)^*$ is denoted by A^{**}.

5.57 Lemma. *If A is a right ideal in the ring R of all linear transformations of a vector space of finite dimension over a division ring, then $A = A^{**}$.*

Proof: By the preceding lemma, $A = eR$, where e is an idempotent in A. It follows that

$$A^* = \{x \mid x \in V, \, xe = 0\}.$$

Let $\{x_1, \ldots, x_k\}$ be a basis of the subspace A^* and extend it to a basis $\{x_1, \ldots, x_k, \ldots, x_n\}$ of V. Then, using definition 5.48, it is clear that

$$A^{**} = \{r \mid r \in R, \, x_i r = 0 \ (i = 1, 2, \ldots, k)\}.$$

Now the vectors $x_{k+1}e, \ldots, x_n e$ are linearly independent (why?). Let $r \in A^{**}$. Then, by the density of R, there is an element s of R such that $x_i es = x_i r$ $(i = k + 1, \ldots, n)$. Also this equation holds for $i = 1, 2, \ldots, k$ since both sides are zero. It follows that $xes = xr$ for all $x \in V$, that is, that $es = r$. This shows that $r \in A$ and hence that $A^{**} \subseteq A$. However, it is always true that $A \subseteq A^{**}$, so we have $A = A^{**}$ and the proof is completed.

In the notation of the above proof there is a tacit assumption that $k \neq 0$ and $k \neq n$. We leave it to the reader to verify that the final result holds in these special cases as well.

The result just established shows that the right ideals in R are just the annihilating right ideals of the subspaces of V. Moreover, this result combined with the result of Lemma 5.50 shows that if V has finite dimension, there exists a *one-one* mapping $A \to A^*$ (or $W^* \to W$) of the right ideals in R onto the subspaces of V. Moreover, $A \subset B$ if and only if $B^* \subset A^*$. This implies that both the d.c.c. and the a.c.c. for right ideals hold in R, since V has finite dimension and cannot have an infinite increasing or decreasing chain of subspaces. In fact, this argument establishes the following somewhat more precise result.

5.58   Theorem.   *There are at most n + 1 right ideals in any strictly increasing (or decreasing) chain of right ideals in a complete matrix ring D_n over a division ring D.*

30. THE WEDDERBURN-ARTIN THEOREM

Throughout this section we shall assume that the d.c.c. for right ideals holds in the ring R. We have proved in Theorem 4.30 that in such a ring every nil right ideal is nilpotent. Moreover, Corollary 4.31 shows that the prime radical $\mathfrak{P}(R)$ of R is the (unique) maximal nilpotent ideal in R (containing every nilpotent right, or left, ideal in R). Historically, the concept of radical of a ring was first introduced only for rings R in which the d.c.c. (and also the a.c.c.) holds for right ideals, and the radical was then *defined* to be the maximal nilpotent ideal in R. Other definitions of radical of a ring, such as the prime radical and two additional radicals to be presented in later chapters, have been introduced in an attempt to obtain a concept which is meaningful for arbitrary rings and which concides with the maximal nilpotent ideal in the presence of the d.c.c. for right ideals. Since all these concepts of radical coincide if the d.c.c. for right ideals holds in R, in the statement of the next theorem we shall refer simply to the *radical* of R. In particular, if the d.c.c. for right ideals holds in R, R has zero radical if and only if it contains no nonzero nilpotent right (or left) ideal.

We shall next prove the celebrated Wedderburn-Artin theorem. Historically, its proof represented a fundamental advance in the knowledge of the structure theory of rings.

5.59   Wedderburn-Artin Theorem.   *Let R be a nonzero ring such that the d.c.c. for right ideals holds in R. Then R has zero radical if and only if R is isomorphic to a direct sum of a finite number of rings, each of which is a complete matrix ring over some division ring.*

Proof: In our proof we shall make use of previously established properties of the *prime* radical. If n is a positive integer and D a division ring, the simple ring D_n is a prime ring since $D_n^2 \neq (0)$. If, then, R is isomorphic to a direct sum of rings of this type, Theorem 4.27 shows that $\mathfrak{P}(R) = (0)$. This establishes one part of the theorem.

Suppose, now, that $\mathfrak{P}(R) = (0)$. If P_i, $i \in \mathfrak{A}$, are the prime ideals in R, Theorem 4.7 shows that $\bigcap\limits_{i \in \mathfrak{A}} P_i = (0)$. We now assert that there must exist a finite number k of prime ideals in R having zero intersection. If (0) is a prime ideal, we are through, with $k = 1$. If (0) is not a prime ideal and P_1 is a nonzero prime ideal, then P_1 cannot be contained in all other prime ideals since the intersection of all of them is zero. Suppose that $P_1 \nsubseteq P_2$, so that $P_1 \supset P_1 \cap P_2$. If $P_1 \cap P_2 \neq (0)$, there must exist a prime ideal P_3 such that $P_1 \cap P_2 \nsubseteq P_3$, so we have

$$P_1 \supset P_1 \cap P_2 \supset P_1 \cap P_2 \cap P_3.$$

If $P_1 \cap P_2 \cap P_3 \neq (0)$, this process can be continued, and so on. However, any decreasing chain of ideals must contain only a finite number of ideals, so for some positive integer k and proper choice of notation we must have $\bigcap\limits_{i=1}^{k} P_i = (0)$. Clearly, we may assume that $P_i \neq R$ $(i = 1, 2, \ldots, k)$, and Corollary 5.55 then shows that the P_i are maximal ideals in R and that each ring R/P_i is isomorphic to a complete matrix ring over a division ring. Theorem 3.18 then asserts that R is isomorphic to a direct sum of a finite number of rings, each of which is a complete matrix ring over a division ring. The proof of the theorem is therefore completed.

We collect in the next theorem a number of results which follow fairly easily from the theorem just established. They could be established by more direct methods, but now that the Wedderburn-Artin Theorem is available we may as well make use of it.

5.60 Theorem. *Let R be a ring with more than one element such that the d.c.c. for right ideals holds in R, and R has zero radical. Then each of the following is true:*

(i) *R has a unity.*

(ii) *R is a simple ring if and only if it is a prime (or primitive) ring.*

(iii) *R is expressible as a direct sum of a finite number of minimal right ideals.*

(iv) *Each right ideal in R is a direct summand.*

(v) *Each right ideal in R is of the form eR for an idempotent e.*

Proof: By Lemma 5.56, properties (iv) and (v) follow from properties (i) and (iii); so we only need to prove the first three parts of the theorem.

By the Wedderburn-Artin Theorem, there exist ideals† U_i ($i = 1, 2,$ $\ldots, k$) in R such that

5.61 $$R = U_1 \oplus U_2 \oplus \cdots \oplus U_k,$$

each U_i being isomorphic to a complete matrix ring D_n for some positive integer n and some division ring D. If $i \neq j$, then $U_i \cap U_j = (0)$, and therefore $U_i U_j = (0)$. We now prove in turn the first three parts of the theorem.

Proof of (i)*:* Since D_n has a unity, so does each ring U_i in 5.61. If e_i is the unity of U_i ($i = 1, 2, \ldots, k$), then $e = e_1 + e_2 + \cdots + e_k$ is a unity for R. For each element of R is expressible in the form $r = u_1 + u_2 + \cdots + u_k$, where $u_i \in U_i$ ($i = 1, 2, \ldots, k$), and since $e_i u_j = u_j e_i = 0$ for $i \neq j$, it follows that $er = re = r$.

Proof of (ii)*:* In 5.61, R is a simple ring if and only if $k = 1$. Similarly, since $U_i U_j = (0)$ for $i \neq j$, R is a prime ring if and only if $k = 1$. In the presence of the d.c.c. for right ideals we already know (5.20, Exercise 7, and 5.28) that a ring is prime if and only if it is primitive.

Proof of (iii)*:* In 2.29, Exercise 4, it was shown that D_n is expressible as a direct sum of minimal right ideals; hence the same is true for each U_i in 5.61. However, it is easily seen that a minimal right ideal in the ring U_i is actually a minimal right ideal in R. The desired result follows by replacing each U_i in 5.61 by a direct sum of minimal right ideals.

Some additional applications of the Wedderburn-Artin Theorem will appear in the exercises below.

5.62   EXERCISES

1. If U_1 and U_2 are subspaces of a vector space V, the sum $U_1 + U_2$ is said to be a *direct sum* and we write $U_1 \oplus U_2$ if each element of $U_1 + U_2$ is uniquely expressible in the form $u_1 + u_2$, with $u_1 \in U_1$ and $u_2 \in U_2$.

  (i) Prove that the sum $U_1 + U_2$ is a direct sum if and only if $U_1 \cap U_2 = 0$.

  (ii) If U_1 is an arbitrary subspace of V, prove that there exists a subspace U_2 of V such that $V = U_1 \oplus U_2$.

---

† In Theorem 3.18, which was used in the final step of the proof of the Wedderburn-Artin Theorem, the elements of a direct sum were considered to be k-tuples with componentwise addition and multiplication. However, it was pointed out following the proof of Theorem 2.13 that if S is such a direct sum, S can also be expressed as a direct sum of corresponding *ideals* in S. It is this viewpoint which we shall use here.

(iii) Show by means of an example that the subspace U_2 of the preceding part need not be unique.

2. Let R be a ring of linear transformations of a vector space V over a division ring. If a and b are elements of R of finite rank and c is an arbitrary element of R, prove each of the following:

(i) Both ac and ca have finite rank.

(ii) The rank of ab does not exceed the rank of a or the rank of b.

(iii) The rank of $a + b$ does not exceed the sum of the ranks of a and of b.

3. Let V be a vector space with a denumerable basis and let K be defined as in Example 3, page 96. Moreover, let S be the ring of all linear transformations of V and T the ring of all elements of S of finite rank. Show that $K \subset T \subset S$.

4. Let R be a ring with more than one element such that the d.c.c. for right ideals holds in R. Prove that R is isomorphic to a direct sum of a finite number of division rings if and only if R has no nonzero nilpotent elements.

5. If a ring R has zero radical and the d.c.c. for right ideals holds in R, show that the a.c.c. for right ideals also holds in R.

6. Let D and D' be anti-isomorphic division rings, with the anti-isomorphism represented by $\alpha \to \alpha'$, $\alpha \in D$. If $A = (\alpha_{ij})$ is an element of D_n, let $A' = (\alpha'_{ij}) \in D'_n$. If the transpose of A' (that is, the matrix obtained from A' by interchanging rows and columns) is denoted by $(A')^T$, verify that the mapping $A \to (A')^T$, $A \in D_n$, is an anti-isomorphism of D_n onto D'_n.

7. Verify that under an anti-isomorphism left ideals map into right ideals, and vice versa. Hence apply the result of the preceding exercise and Theorem 5.58 to show that a result analogous to Theorem 5.58 holds also for *left* ideals.

8. If a ring R has zero radical and the d.c.c. for right ideals holds in R, prove that both the d.c.c. and the a.c.c. for left ideals hold in R.

CHAPTER 6

The Jacobson Radical

IN THIS CHAPTER we introduce and briefly discuss the important concept of the Jacobson radical of a ring. There are several possible definitions of this concept which, although seemingly quite different, can be shown to be equivalent. We choose to start with one of the most elementary of these definitions and proceed to prove several important properties.

31. PRELIMINARY CONCEPTS

We begin by defining on a ring R a new binary operation $\circ$ as follows. If $a, b \in R$, we define

$$a \circ b = a + b - ab.$$

We leave it to the reader to verify that $\circ$ is an associative operation and that 0 is an identity for this operation, that is, that

$$a \circ 0 = 0 \circ a = a$$

for every element a of R.

It is important to observe that if R has a unity 1, then $a \circ b = 0$ if and only if $(1 - a)(1 - b) = 1$. This fact furnishes at least a partial motivation of some of the material below.

We now let R be an arbitrary ring and define several new terms as follows.

6.1 Definition. Let a be an element of the ring R.

(i) If there exists an element b of R such that $a \circ b = 0$, a is said to be *right quasi-regular* (r.q.r.) and to have b as a *right quasi-inverse* (r.q.i.).

(ii) If there exists an element c of R such that $c \circ a = 0$, a is said to be *left quasi-regular* (l.q.r.) and to have c as a *left quasi-inverse* (l.q.i.).

(iii) The element a is said to be *quasi-regular* (q.r.) if it is both r.q.r. and l.q.r.

(iv) An element d of R is said to be a *quasi-inverse* (q.i.) of a if d is a r.q.i. of a and also a l.q.i. of a.

(v) A right ideal or left ideal in R is said to be r.q.r. (l.q.r. or q.r., respectively) if each of its elements is r.q.r. (l.q.r. or q.r., respectively).

If R has a unity 1, it is clear that a has a r.q.i. (l.q.i. or q.i., respectively) if and only if $1 - a$ has a right inverse (left inverse or inverse, respectively).

We now observe that *if an element a of R has a r.q.i. b and also a l.q.i. c, then $b = c$.* For if $a \circ b = c \circ a = 0$, we see that

$$c = c \circ 0 = c \circ (a \circ b) = (c \circ a) \circ b = 0 \circ b = b.$$

Incidentally, this same calculation shows that *if an element has a q.i., it is unique*; also that if it has more than one r.q.i., it has no l.q.i., and vice versa.

We proceed to establish several lemmas which will be useful in the sequel.

6.2 Lemma. *Every nilpotent element of a ring is quasi-regular.*

If $a^n = 0$ and we set $b = - \sum_{k=1}^{n-1} a^k$, a simple calculation will verify that $a \circ b = b \circ a = 0$.

6.3 Lemma. *An element a of the ring R is right quasi-regular if and only if the right ideal $A = \{ax - x \mid x \in R\}$ coincides with R.*

First, if $A = R$, there exists $y \in R$ such that $a = ay - y$, or $a \circ y = 0$.

Next, if there exists $y \in R$ such that $a \circ y = 0$, we have $a + y - ay = 0$ and $a \in A$. For each $x \in R$, we then have $ax \in A$. But $ax - x \in A$, and we conclude that $x \in A$. Hence $R \subseteq A$ and therefore $R = A$.

6.4 Lemma. *If $a, b \in R$ such that ab is right quasi-regular, then ba is right quasi-regular.*

If $(ab) \circ c = ab + c - abc = 0$, it is easy to verify that

$$(ba) \circ (-ba + bca) = b[(ab) \circ c]a = 0,$$

and ba has $-ba + bca$ as r.q.i.

6.5   Lemma.   *If a right ideal A in R is right quasi-regular, it is quasi-regular.*

If $a \in A$, there exists $b \in R$ such that $a \circ b = 0$. Thus b has a as l.q.i. But $b \in A$ since $b = ab - a$, so b has a r.q.i. by hypothesis, which necessarily coincides with a. It follows that $b \circ a = 0 = a \circ b$, which shows that a and b are quasi-inverses of each other and hence that a is quasi-regular.

In view of this last lemma, it might be well to state than an individual element of a ring R may be r.q.r. but not q.r. If R has a unity, this is equivalent to saying that there may exist in R an element which has a right inverse but no inverse. For an example, see 6.27, Exercise 12.

32. DEFINITION AND SIMPLE PROPERTIES

We next make the following definition.

6.6   Definition.   The *Jacobson radical* $\mathfrak{J}(R)$ of a ring R is defined as follows:

$$\mathfrak{J}(R) = \{a \mid a \in R, \, aR \text{ is r.q.r.}\}.$$

It is important to keep in mind that, in view of Lemma 6.5, we could just as well require that aR be q.r. in the definition of $\mathfrak{J}(R)$.

6.7   Theorem. $\mathfrak{J}(R)$ *is a quasi-regular ideal in R which contains every quasi-regular right ideal and every quasi-regular left ideal in R.*

Proof: Let us first prove that $\mathfrak{J}(R)$ is an ideal in R and, for convenience, let us also denote $\mathfrak{J}(R)$ by $\mathfrak{J}$. If $a \in \mathfrak{J}$ so that aR is r.q.r., then for each x in R we have $(ax)R \subseteq aR$, so $(ax)R$ is r.q.r. and $ax \in \mathfrak{J}$. Now for each $x, y \in R$, it follows from what we have just proved that ayx is r.q.r. and Lemma 6.4 shows that xay is r.q.r. That is, xaR is r.q.r. and

$xa \in \mathfrak{F}$. There remains to show that if a, $b \in \mathfrak{F}$, then $a - b \in \mathfrak{F}$. If $x \in R$, suppose that a' is a r.q.i. of ax, so that $ax \circ a' = 0$. Since $b \in \mathfrak{F}$, $b(-x + xa')$ is r.q.r., and hence there exists an element w' of R such that $[b(-x + xa')] \circ w' = 0$. It follows that

$$
\begin{aligned}
[(a - b)x] \circ (a' \circ w') &= ([(a - b)x] \circ a') \circ w' \\
&= [(a - b)x + a' - (a - b)xa'] \circ w' \\
&= [(ax \circ a') + b(-x + xa')] \circ w' \\
&= [b(-x + xa')] \circ w' = 0.
\end{aligned}
$$

This proves that $(a - b)R$ is r.q.r., and hence that $a - b \in \mathfrak{F}$. Therefore, $\mathfrak{F}(R)$ is an ideal in R.

In view of Lemma 6.5, we can show that $\mathfrak{F}(R)$ is a quasi-regular ideal by showing that each element is right quasi-regular. If $a \in \mathfrak{F}$, then aR is r.q.r. and, in particular, a^2 is r.q.r. Suppose that $a^2 \circ c = 0$. Then

$$
a \circ [(-a) \circ c] = [a \circ (-a)] \circ c = a^2 \circ c = 0,
$$

and a has $(-a) \circ c$ as r.q.i., so that $\mathfrak{F}(R)$ is a quasi-regular ideal.

If A is a quasi-regular right ideal in R and $a \in A$, then $aR \subseteq A$ and $a \in \mathfrak{F}(R)$ by Definition 6.6. Hence $A \subseteq \mathfrak{F}(R)$.

If A is a quasi-regular left ideal in R and $a \in A$, then $Ra \subseteq A$ and Ra is quasi-regular. Lemmas 6.4 and 6.5 show that aR is quasi-regular, and hence that $a \in \mathfrak{F}(R)$. Thus $A \subseteq \mathfrak{F}(R)$. This completes the proof of the theorem.

In view of this theorem, we see that $\mathfrak{F}(R)$ is the unique largest quasi-regular ideal of R and that it can be characterized as the sum of all quasi-regular right ideals in R (or the sum of all quasi-regular left ideals in R).

The following result is an immediate consequence of Lemma 6.2.

6.8 Corollary. $\mathfrak{F}(R)$ *contains every nil right (or left) ideal in* R.

Let us now give a simple example to show that the Jacobson radical, even when not zero, need not contain any nonzero nilpotent elements. Let S be the ring of those rational numbers which can be expressed in the form i/m, where i is an arbitrary integer and m is an *odd* integer. The equation

$$
\frac{2i}{m} + \frac{(-2i)}{m - 2i} - \left(\frac{2i}{m}\right)\left(\frac{-2i}{m - 2i}\right) = 0
$$

shows that $2x$ is q.r. for every $x = i/m$ in S; hence that $2 \in \Im(S)$. Clearly, S itself has no nonzero nilpotent elements since it is a subring of the field of rational numbers. Actually, 6.27, Exercise 11, shows that $\Im(S) = (2)$.

We shall next prove the following result.

6.9   Theorem.   *If $\Im(R)$ is the Jacobson radical of the ring R, then $\Im(R/\Im(R)) = (0)$.*

Proof: For simplicity of notation, let us denote $\Im(R)$ by $\Im$. Suppose that $a + \Im \in \Im(R/\Im)$. Then for each $x \in R$, $(a + \Im)(x + \Im)$ is r.q.r. in $R/\Im$. Thus there is an element $s + \Im$ of $R/\Im$ such that

$$[(a + \Im)(x + \Im)] \circ [s + \Im] = \Im.$$

However, this equation implies that $(ax \circ s) \in \Im$ and therefore that there exists $t \in R$ such that $(ax \circ s) \circ t = 0$. By the associativity of $\circ$, it follows that ax has $s \circ t$ as r.q.i. in R. That is, aR is r.q.r. and hence $a \in \Im$. This shows that $a + \Im$ is the zero of the ring $R/\Im$, and completes the proof.

This theorem, together with Corollary 6.8, shows that the ring $R/\Im(R)$ contains no nonzero nil right or left ideals. In particular, it contains no nonzero nilpotent ideals and Theorem 4.11 then yields the following result.

6.10   Corollary.   *$\Im(R)$ is a semi-prime ideal in the ring R.*

The following result now follows immediately from Theorem 4.20(ii).

6.11   Corollary.   *If $\mathfrak{P}(R)$ and $\Im(R)$ are, respectively, the prime radical and the Jacobson radical of the ring R, then $\mathfrak{P}(R) \subseteq \Im(R)$.*

Incidentally, the ring S of the example following Corollary 6.8 is an integral domain and hence $\mathfrak{P}(S) = (0)$. For this ring, we therefore have $\mathfrak{P}(S) \subset \Im(S)$.

If $a \in R$ such that $RaR \subseteq \Im(R)$, then $(aR)^2 \subseteq \Im(R)$ and Corollary 6.10 shows that $aR \subseteq \Im(R)$. Hence aR is quasi-regular and $a \in \Im(R)$. We have therefore established the following fact.

6.12   Corollary.   *If $a \in R$ such that $RaR \subseteq \Im(R)$, then $a \in \Im(R)$.*

We next prove the following simple result which will be needed in the next section.

6.13   Lemma.   *If θ is a homomorphism of the ring R onto the ring S, then $\mathfrak{J}(R)\theta \subseteq \mathfrak{J}(S)$.*

Proof: If $a, b \in R$, then

$$(a \circ b)\theta = (a + b - ab)\theta = a\theta + b\theta - (a\theta)(b\theta) = (a\theta) \circ (b\theta),$$

and the operation $\circ$ is preserved under the mapping θ. In particular, if $a \circ b = 0$, then also $(a\theta) \circ (b\theta) = 0$. It follows that $\mathfrak{J}(R)\theta$ is a quasi-regular ideal in S and hence, by Theorem 6.7, that $\mathfrak{J}(R)\theta \subseteq \mathfrak{J}(S)$.

We shall conclude this section by proving two results about the Jacobson radical of related rings. It will be observed that these take the same form as corresponding results about the prime radical which were established in Chapter 4 (Theorems 4.23 and 4.29).

6.14   Theorem.   *If S is an ideal in the ring R, then $\mathfrak{J}(S) = S \cap \mathfrak{J}(R)$.*

Proof: Suppose, first, that $a \in S \cap \mathfrak{J}(R)$. Since $a \in \mathfrak{J}(R)$, ax is r.q.r. for each x in R and there exists $y \in R$ such that $ax + y - axy = 0$. This equation shows that $y \in S$ since $a \in S$. In particular, aS is right quasi-regular *in the ring S*, and therefore $a \in \mathfrak{J}(S)$. This shows that $S \cap \mathfrak{J}(R) \subseteq \mathfrak{J}(S)$.

Conversely, suppose that $a \in \mathfrak{J}(S)$. Since $(aR)^2 \subseteq aS$, $(aR)^2$ is a quasi-regular right ideal in R and hence $(aR)^2 \subseteq \mathfrak{J}(R)$. Corollary 6.10 then shows that $aR \subseteq \mathfrak{J}(R)$ and this implies that $a \in \mathfrak{J}(R)$. We have shown that $\mathfrak{J}(S) \subseteq S \cap \mathfrak{J}(R)$, and the proof is completed.

6.15   Theorem.   *If R_n is the ring of all matrices of order n over the ring R, then $\mathfrak{J}(R_n) = (\mathfrak{J}(R))_n$.*

Proof: First, consider a matrix of R_n of the form

$$Y = \begin{bmatrix} y_{11} & y_{12} & \cdots & y_{1n} \\ 0 & 0 & \cdots & 0 \\ \cdot & \cdot & \cdots & \cdot \\ 0 & 0 & \cdots & 0 \end{bmatrix}$$

in which all elements are zero in rows other than the first, and suppose that y_{11} is right quasi-regular. Thus there exists $y'_{11} \in R$ such that $y_{11} \circ y'_{11} = 0$. Also, by Lemma 6.3, we have that

$$\{y_{11}x - x \mid x \in R\} = R.$$

Hence there exist elements y'_{1i} of R such that

$$y_{11}y'_{1i} - y'_{1i} = y_{1i}, \qquad\qquad i = 2, 3, \ldots, n.$$

If we set

$$Y' = \begin{bmatrix} y'_{11} & y'_{12} & \cdots & y'_{1n} \\ 0 & 0 & \cdots & 0 \\ \cdot & \cdot & & \cdot \\ 0 & 0 & \cdots & 0 \end{bmatrix},$$

then $Y \circ Y' = 0$ and Y is therefore r.q.r. in R_n.

Now let A_i be the set of all matrices of $(\mathfrak{J}(R))_n$ which have zeros everywhere except possibly in the ith row $(i = 1, 2, \ldots, n)$. By the argument above, every element of A_1 is r.q.r. in R_n. However, not only is A_1 a right ideal in $(\mathfrak{J}(R))_n$ but it is also a right ideal in R_n and hence (by 6.5 and 6.7) we must have $A_1 \subseteq \mathfrak{J}(R_n)$. A similar argument will show that $A_i \subseteq \mathfrak{J}(R_n)$ for $i = 2, 3, \ldots, n$. Since $(\mathfrak{J}(R))_n = A_1 \oplus A_2 \oplus \cdots \oplus A_n$, it follows that $(\mathfrak{J}(R))_n \subseteq \mathfrak{J}(R_n)$.

To obtain inclusion the other way, suppose that† $Z = (z_{ij}) = \sum z_{ij}E_{ij}$ is an element of $\mathfrak{J}(R_n)$. Then, for arbitrary elements x and y of R and arbitrary integers p and q $(1 \le p \le n, 1 \le q \le n)$, we have

$$xE_{1p}ZyE_{q1} = xz_{pq}yE_{11} \in \mathfrak{J}(R_n).$$

If $T = (t_{ij})$ is a right quasi-inverse of $xz_{pq}yE_{11}$ in R_n, a consideration of elements in the first row and first column will show that t_{11} is a right quasi-inverse of $xz_{pq}y$ in R. This shows that the ideal $Rz_{pq}R$ is r.q.r. By Theorem 6.7, it follows that $Rz_{pq}R \subseteq \mathfrak{J}(R)$, and Corollary 6.12 then shows that $z_{pq} \in \mathfrak{J}(R)$. This proves that $Z \in (\mathfrak{J}(R))_n$, and we have $\mathfrak{J}(R_n) \subseteq (\mathfrak{J}(R))_n$. This completes the proof of the theorem.

---

† We are here using the matrix units in a formal way and are not assuming that R necessarily has a unity. If $a \in R$, aE_{ij} is to be interpreted as the matrix with a at the intersection of the ith row and j^{th} column, and zeros elsewhere.

33. FURTHER PROPERTIES OF THE JACOBSON RADICAL

In this section we shall indicate how the Jacobson radical of a ring is related to some of the important concepts of the preceding chapter. First, we shall prove the following result.

6.16 Theorem. *If R is a primitive ring, then* $\Im(R) = (0)$.

Proof: We may just as well assume that R is itself an irreducible ring of endomorphisms of an abelian group V (not just isomorphic to such a ring). Let $a \in \Im(R)$ and suppose that $xa \neq 0$ for some $x \in V$. Then $(xa)R = V$ by Lemma 5.17. Hence there exists $b \in R$ such that $x(ab) = x$. Since $a \in \Im(R)$, ab is right quasi-regular and there exists $c \in R$ such that $ab + c - abc = 0$. It follows that

$$x = x - x(ab + c - abc) = x - x(ab) - [x - x(ab)]c = 0,$$

and the assumption that $xa \neq 0$ has led to a contradiction. Hence $xa = 0$ for every $x \in V$, which implies that $a = 0$. This shows that $\Im(R) = (0)$ and the proof is completed.

6.17 Lemma. *If A is a modular maximal right ideal in a ring R, then* $\Im(R) \subseteq (A:R)$.

Proof: By Theorem 5.34, $R/(A:R)$ is a primitive ring and therefore this ring has zero Jacobson radical. If θ is the natural homomorphism of R onto $R/(A:R)$, Lemma 6.13 shows that $\Im(R)\theta = 0$ and hence that $\Im(R)$ is contained in the kernel $(A:R)$ of this homomorphism.

6.18 Lemma. *If $a \in R$ and a is not right quasi-regular, there exists in R a modular maximal right ideal A such that $a \notin A$.*

Proof: Since a is not r.q.r., the right ideal $B = \{ar - r \mid r \in R\}$ does not contain a. Then Zorn's Lemma shows the existence of a right ideal A which is maximal in the set of those right ideals which contain B but not the element a. Now A is actually a maximal right ideal in R, for if A_1 is a right ideal such that $A \subset A_1$, then $a \in A_1$ and $ar - r \in A_1$ for each $r \in R$. It follows that $A_1 = R$, and A is indeed a maximal right ideal in R. Moreover, A is modular since $ar - r \in A$ for every $r \in R$. The lemma is therefore established.

6.19   Lemma.   *If $b \in R$ such that $b \notin \Im(R)$, then there exists in R a modular maximal right ideal which does not contain b.*

Proof: If $b \notin \Im(R)$, there exists $t \in R$ such that bt is not r.q.r. The preceding lemma shows that there exists in R a modular maximal right ideal which does not contain bt and therefore does not contain b.

We are now ready to prove the following theorem.

6.20   Theorem.   *Let R be a ring such that $\Im(R) \neq R$, and let A_i, $i \in \mathfrak{A}$, be all the modular maximal right ideals in R. Then*

$$\text{(a)} \quad \Im(R) = \bigcap_{i \in \mathfrak{A}} A_i,$$

and

$$\text{(b)} \quad \Im(R) = \bigcap_{i \in \mathfrak{A}} (A_i : R).$$

Proof: Since $\Im(R) \neq R$, Lemma 6.19 shows that there actually exist modular maximal right ideals A_i in R and that $\cap A_i \subseteq \Im(R)$. By Lemma 6.17, we have $\Im(R) \subseteq \cap (A_i : R)$ and hence $R\Im(R) \subseteq A_i$ for each $i \in \mathfrak{A}$. Since each A_i is modular, it follows that $\Im(R) \subseteq A_i$ and therefore that $\Im(R) \subseteq \cap A_i$. We have therefore established the first part of the theorem. Now since A_i is modular, it is easy to verify (cf. 5.36, Exercise 2) that $(A_i : R) \subseteq A_i$. Hence

$$\cap(A_i : R) \subseteq \cap A_i = \Im(R)$$

by part (a) of the theorem. We have now obtained inclusion both ways, so we conclude that $\Im(R) = \cap(A_i : R)$, and the proof is completed.

One interesting consequence of this theorem is that if $\Im(R) \neq R$, then the intersection of all modular maximal right ideals in R is a two-sided ideal in R. As a special case, if R has more than one element and has a unity 1, then 1 cannot be quasi-regular and therefore $\Im(R) \neq R$. Moreover, every right ideal is modular, so that in this case the intersection of *all* maximal right ideals in R is a two-sided ideal in R.

The following important property is sometimes taken as the *definition* of the Jacobson radical. Of course, if that approach were used, our definition would take the form of a theorem.

6.21   Theorem.   *If $a \in R$, then $a \in \Im(R)$ if and only if a is in the kernel of every homomorphism of R onto a primitive ring.*

Proof: If θ is a homomorphism of R onto a primitive ring, then $\Im(R)\theta = (0)$ by Theorem 6.16 and Lemma 6.13. Therefore $\Im(R)$ is in the kernel of the homomorphism θ.

To prove the converse, suppose that $a \in R$ is in the kernel of every homomorphism of R onto a primitive ring, and let us show that $a \in \mathfrak{I}(R)$. If $\mathfrak{I}(R) = R$, the desired result is trivial. If $\mathfrak{I}(R) \neq R$, let A_i, $i \in \mathfrak{A}$, be the modular maximal right ideals in R. By hypothesis and Theorem 5.34, for each $i \in \mathfrak{A}$ we have that a is in the kernel $(A_i : R)$ of the natural homomorphism of R onto the primitive ring $R/(A_i : R)$. Theorem 6.20(b) then shows that $a \in \mathfrak{I}(R)$, and the proof is completed.

The relation of the Jacobson radical to the concept of subdirect sum is brought out in the following theorem.

6.22 Theorem. *If R is a ring with more than one element, then $\mathfrak{I}(R) = (0)$ if and only if R is isomorphic to a subdirect sum of primitive rings.*

Proof: Suppose, first, that $\mathfrak{I}(R) = (0)$. Then $\mathfrak{I}(R) \neq R$, and Theorem 6.20(b) shows that if A_i, $i \in \mathfrak{A}$, are the modular maximal right ideals in R, then $\cap(A_i : R) = (0)$. By Theorem 3.9, we find that R is isomorphic to a subdirect sum of the rings $R/(A_i : R)$ and these rings are primitive by Theorem 5.34.

Conversely, suppose that R is isomorphic to a subdirect sum of primitive rings S_i, $i \in \mathfrak{A}$. By Theorem 3.6, there exist homomorphisms ϕ_i of R onto S_i, $i \in \mathfrak{A}$, such that if r is a nonzero element of R, then $r\phi_i \neq 0$ for at least one $i \in \mathfrak{A}$. However, if $a \in \mathfrak{I}(R)$, then $a\phi_i = 0$ for every $i \in \mathfrak{A}$ by Theorem 6.21. Accordingly, we must have $a = 0$. Hence $\mathfrak{I}(R) = (0)$ and the proof is completed.

By 5.20, Exercises 5 and 6, the commutative primitive rings are the fields. Using this fact, we have the following immediate consequence of the preceding theorem.

6.23 Corollary. *A commutative ring R with more than one element is isomorphic to a subdirect sum of fields if and only if $\mathfrak{I}(R) = (0)$.*

34. THE DESCENDING CHAIN CONDITION

We conclude our discussion of the Jacobson radical by considering the effect of the d.c.c. for right ideals. The principal result is the following.

6.24   Theorem.   *If the d.c.c. for right ideals holds in the ring R, then $\mathfrak{J}(R)$ is nilpotent.*

Proof: Suppose that N is a two-sided ideal of R such that $N \subseteq \mathfrak{J}(R)$ and $N^2 = N$. If $N \neq (0)$, consider the set of those right ideals A of R such that $A \subseteq N$ and $AN \neq (0)$. This set is not empty since it contains N, and the d.c.c. assures us that there exists a right ideal B which is minimal in this set. Thus there exists $b \in B$ such that $bN \neq (0)$. Then $(bN)N = bN \neq 0$ and since $bN \subseteq B$ the minimal property of B assures us that $bN = B$. It follows that there exists an element y of N such that $by = b$. Since $N \subseteq \mathfrak{J}(R)$, y is r.q.r. and there exists $t \in R$ such that $y + t - yt = 0$. Hence we have

$$0 = b - by - (b - by)t = b - b(y + t - yt) = b,$$

contrary to $bN \neq (0)$. Our assumption that $N \neq (0)$ has led to a contradiction, and we conclude that $N = (0)$. Now, writing $\mathfrak{J}$ for $\mathfrak{J}(R)$, it is clear that

$$\mathfrak{J} \supseteq \mathfrak{J}^2 \supseteq \mathfrak{J}^3 \supseteq \cdots,$$

and, since we are assuming the d.c.c., there must exist a positive integer n such that $\mathfrak{J}^n = \mathfrak{J}^{n+1} = \mathfrak{J}^{n+2} = \cdots$. If we set $N = \mathfrak{J}^n$, then $N \subseteq \mathfrak{J}$ and $N^2 = N$, and our proof above shows that $N = (0)$. Therefore, $\mathfrak{J}$ is nilpotent and the theorem is established.

By Corollary 6.8, $\mathfrak{J}(R)$ contains every nil right or left ideal in R. Accordingly, we have immediately the following result.

6.25   Corollary.   *If the d.c.c. for right ideals holds in the ring R, then every nil right or left ideal in R is nilpotent.*

We may point out that the proof of this result is independent of the proof of Theorem 4.30 in which it was proved that in the presence of the d.c.c. for right ideals every nil *right* ideal is nilpotent.

Finally, we observe that the theorem of this section together with Corollaries 6.11 and 4.31 yield at once the following result.

6.26   Corollary.   *If the d.c.c. for right ideals holds in the ring R, then the Jacobson radical of R coincides with the prime radical of R.*

6.27   EXERCISES

1. If c and d are elements of a ring R, prove each of the following.

(i) If c has d as a q.i., then c commutes with d.

(ii) If c has d as a r.q.i. and c commutes with d, then d is a q.i. of c.

2. Show that the set of all q.r. elements of a ring R is a group with respect to the operation $\circ$.

3. Prove that if $a \in R$ is such that a^n is r.q.r. for some positive integer n, then a is r.q.r.

4. Prove that a nonzero idempotent cannot be r.q.r. or l.q.r. This implies that $\Im(R)$ contains no nonzero idempotents.

5. Show that if $a, b \in R$ such that $a = ab$ and b is r.q.r., then $a = 0$.

6. If e is an idempotent in the ring R, then eRe is a subring of R. Show that $\Im(eRe) = e\Im(R)e$.

7. If K is a two-sided ideal in the ring R such that $K \subseteq \Im(R)$, show that $\Im(R/K) = \Im(R)/K$.

8. Show that if $\Im(R) = R$, then R contains no modular maximal right ideal.

9. If R is an arbitrary ring, prove that $\Im(\Im(R)) = \Im(R)$.

10. If the ring R without unity is imbedded in a ring S with unity by the method of Section 2, show that $\Im(R) = \Im(S)$.

11. Suppose that R is a ring with unity with the property that the set K of all elements of R which do not have inverses is an ideal in R. Prove that $K = \Im(R)$.

12. Let V be a vector space over a division ring D, and suppose that V has a denumerable basis $z_1, z_2, z_3, \cdots$. Let R be the ring of all linear transformations of V, and define elements a, b, and c of R as follows:

$$z_1a = z_2, \quad z_2a = z_1 + z_3, \quad z_na = z_{n+1}, \qquad (n = 3, 4, \ldots),$$
$$z_1b = 0, \quad z_nb = z_{n-1}, \qquad\qquad\qquad\qquad (n = 2, 3, \ldots),$$
$$z_1c = z_2, \quad z_2c = z_1, \quad z_3c = 0, \quad z_nc = z_{n-1}, \quad (n = 4, 5, \ldots).$$

Verify that both b and c are right inverses of a in R. How do you know that a can have no left inverse in R? If 1 is the unity of R, show that $1 - a$ has two different right quasi-inverses and no left quasi-inverse in R.

CHAPTER 7

Some Additional Topics

IN THIS FINAL chapter we shall present a few additional topics of a somewhat miscellaneous nature. The study of dense rings of linear transformations, which was begun in Chapter 5, will be continued in the first two sections. Finally, in the last section we shall introduce and briefly discuss still another radical of a ring.

35. IDEMPOTENTS AND REGULAR ELEMENTS OF DENSE RINGS

Let V denote a vector space over a division ring D, and let us make the following definition.

7.1 Definition. Let U be a subspace of the vector space V. A linear transformation e of V is called a *projection of V onto U* if $Ve \subseteq U$ and $ye = y$ for each element y of U. A linear transformation is called simply a *projection* if it is a projection of V onto some subspace of V.

If e is a projection of V onto U, we must actually have $Ve = U$ since $Ue = U$. Moreover, it is easy to verify as follows that e must be idempotent. If $x \in V$, we have $xe = u$, where $u \in U$. Hence

$$(xe)e = ue = u = xe,$$

and we have $e^2 = e$. Conversely, we leave it to the reader to verify that a linear transformation e which is idempotent is a projection (of V onto the subspace Ve). Hence a linear transformation is idempotent if and only if it is a projection.

We next introduce another useful concept as follows.

7.2 Definition. Let c be an element of an arbitrary ring R. If there

122

exists an element c' of R such that $c = cc'c$, c is said to be a *regular element* of R. The ring R is said to be a *regular ring* if each of its elements is regular.

If c has an inverse c^{-1}, we have $c = cc^{-1}c$, and c is regular. Moreover, the zero element of every ring is clearly regular. Accordingly, every division ring is a regular ring. The existence of many other regular rings will be established below.

It is easy to verify that if $c = cc'c$, then both cc' and $c'c$ are idempotent. It is this fact which makes the concept of regular element important for our present purposes.

We shall now prove the following result.

7.3 Theorem. *The ring T of all linear transformations of a vector space V over a division ring D is a regular ring.*

Proof: Let a be a nonzero element of T. We recall that the null space V_a of a is the set of all elements y of V such that $ya = 0$. Since $a \neq 0$, we know that $V_a \neq V$. Let Y denote a set of basis elements of V_a and let us extend it (Theorem 5.40) to a basis $X \cup Y$ of V.

If $Xa = \{xa \mid x \in X\}$, the mapping $x \to xa$, $x \in X$, is a one-one mapping of X onto Xa. For if $x_1, x_2 \in X$ such that $x_1a = x_2a$, it follows that $(x_1 - x_2)a = 0$ and $x_1 - x_2 \in V_a$. Hence $x_1 - x_2$ is expressible as a linear combination of elements of the basis Y of V_a, and the linear independence of the set $X \cup Y$ shows that we must have $x_1 = x_2$.

Let us next verify that Xa is a linearly independent set. Suppose that $x_i a$ $(i = 1, 2, \ldots, n)$ are distinct elements of Xa and $\alpha_i \in D$ $(i = 1, 2, \ldots, n)$ such that $\sum (x_i a)\alpha_i = 0$. This implies that $(\sum x_i \alpha_i)a = 0$ and hence that $\sum x_i \alpha_i \in V_a$. However, x_i $(i = 1, 2, \ldots, n)$ are distinct elements of X and again the linear independence of the set $X \cup Y$ shows that $\alpha_i = 0$ $(i = 1, 2, \ldots, n)$. This verifies that Xa is a linearly independent set.

We may now extend the set Xa to a basis $(Xa) \cup Z$ of V. We have observed in Section 26 that there exists a linear transformation of V which maps the elements of a basis $(Xa) \cup Z$ into arbitrary elements of V. Hence there exists an element a' of T (not unique since a' can be arbitrary on Z) such that

$$(xa)a' = x, \qquad\qquad xa \in Xa.$$

Of course, on Xa, a' is just the inverse of the one-one mapping $x \to xa$, $x \in X$. It follows that

$$x(aa'a) = xa, \qquad\qquad x \in X,$$
$$y(aa'a) = 0 = ya, \qquad\qquad y \in Y.$$

Thus the linear transformations a and $aa'a$ have the same effect on all elements of the basis $X \cup Y$ of V, and therefore we have $a = aa'a$. This completes the proof of the theorem.

In the theorem just established we were concerned with the ring of *all* linear transformations of V. Let us now consider merely a dense ring R of linear transformations, but restrict a to be a nonzero element of *finite rank*. Since, in the notation of the above proof, Xa is a basis of the image space Va (for this set is linearly independent and $ya = 0$ for each y in Y), we now have that Xa is a finite set. Accordingly, X is a finite set and the density of R shows that there exists $a' \in R$ such that $(xa)a' = x$ for each x in the set X. It then follows just as above that $a = aa'a$, and a is a regular element of R. We have therefore established the following result.

7.4 Theorem. *If R is a dense ring of linear transformations of a vector space, every element of R of finite rank is regular.*

In view of Theorem 5.52, we have at once the following consequence of either of the preceding theorems.

7.5 Corollary. *For each positive integer n and each division ring D the ring D_n of all matrices of order n over D is a regular ring.*

For later application, we next prove the following result.

7.6 Lemma. *Let R be a dense ring of linear transformations of a vector space V over a division ring D, and let e be an idempotent element of R of finite rank $m > 0$. If U is an arbitrary subspace of V of finite dimension, there exists a projection of V onto U which is an element of the ideal (e).*

Proof: The proof is by induction on the dimension of the subspace U, and let us first assume that U has dimension 1, that is, that $U = yD$ for a nonzero element y of U. Let $\{x_1e, \dots, x_me\}$ be a basis of the image space Ve. By the density of R, there exists an element c of R such that $yc = x_1$ and an element d of R such that

$$x_1ed = y, \qquad x_ied = 0, \qquad (i = 2, \ldots, m).$$

Also, there exists $a \in R$ such that

$$x_1ea = x_1e, \qquad x_iea = 0, \qquad (i = 2, \ldots, m).$$

We proceed to show that *cead* is a projection of V onto $U = yD$. For each $x \in V$, $xce \in Ve$, so xce is expressible as a linear combination $\sum(x_ie)\alpha_i$ of the elements of the basis $\{x_1e, \ldots, x_me\}$ of Ve. Hence we have

$$x(cead) = (\sum(x_ie)\alpha_i)ad = (\sum(x_iea)\alpha_i)d$$
$$= (x_1ea)\alpha_1 d = (x_1ed)\alpha_1 = y\alpha_1 \in U.$$

Moreover,

$$y(cead) = (x_1ea)d = x_1ed = y.$$

These calculations verify that *cead* is a projection of V onto U and, since *cead* is clearly an element of the ideal (e), the proof is completed for the case in which U has dimension 1.

Let us now assume the desired result for every subspace of dimension $k - 1$ and let U be a subspace of dimension k. Suppose that $\{y_1, y_2, \ldots, y_k\}$ is a basis of $U = y_1D + y_2D + \cdots + y_kD$, and let us set $W = y_1D + y_2D + \cdots + y_{k-1}D$. By the induction hypothesis, there exists a projection f of V onto W such that $f \in (e)$. Then $W = Vf$ and $y_i f = y_i$ $(i = 1, 2, \ldots, k - 1)$. Since $y_k f \in Vf$, we may write $y_k f = \sum_{i=1}^{k-1} y_i\alpha_i$. If we set

$$z = y_k - \sum_{i=1}^{k-1} y_i\alpha_i,$$

we see that $zf = 0$, and it is easy to verify that $\{y_1, \ldots, y_{k-1}, z\}$ is a basis of U. It is this basis which we use below. By the case already proved, there exists an element e_1 of (e) which is a projection of V onto zD. We now set $g = f + e_1 - fe_1$, and verify that g is a projection of V onto U. For each $i = 1, \ldots, k - 1$, we have

$$y_i g = y_i f + y_i e_1 - y_i(fe_1) = y_i + y_i e_1 - y_i e_1 = y_i.$$

Also, since $zf = 0$, we have $zg = ze_1 = z$. These calculations show that

$ug = u$ for each element u of a basis of U, and therefore for each element u of U. Moreover, if $x \in V$, it follows that

$$xg = x(f + e_1 - fe_1) = xf + (x - xf)e_1.$$

Since $xf \in W$ and $(x - xf)e_1 \in zD$, we see that $xg \in U$ and thus we have $Vg \subseteq U$. Hence g is indeed a projection of V onto U and the proof is completed since f and e_1 are elements of (e) and therefore also $g \in (e)$.

36. SOME FURTHER RESULTS ON DENSE RINGS

We shall give below one proof of the following theorem. Another proof will be outlined in the notes to this chapter.

7.7   **Theorem.** *If R is a dense ring of linear transformations of a vector space V and K is a nonzero ideal in R, then K is also a dense ring of linear transformations of the same vector space V.*

Proof: If a is a nonzero element of K, there exists $x \in V$ such that $xa \neq 0$ and therefore $(xa)R = V$. Since $aR \subseteq K$, we have $VK = V$. Now suppose that $x_1, x_2, \ldots, x_n$ are linearly independent elements of V, and that $y_1, y_2, \ldots, y_n$ are arbitrary elements of V. We complete the proof by showing that there exists $b \in K$ such that $x_i b = y_i$ ($i = 1, 2, \ldots, n$).

Since $VK = V$, for each $j = 1, 2, \ldots, n$, there exists $z_j \in V$ and $a_j \in K$ such that $z_j a_j = y_j$. Since R is dense, there exists $r_j \in R$ such that $x_j r_j = z_j$ and $x_i r_j = 0$ for $i \neq j$. It follows that $x_j r_j a_j = z_j a_j = y_j$. Let $b = \sum r_j a_j$. Then

$$x_i b = \sum_{j=1}^{n} x_i r_j a_j = x_i r_i a_i = y_i, \qquad (i = 1, 2 \ldots, n).$$

Since $b \in K$, the proof is completed.

Let us now pass to the proof of the following theorem.

7.8   **Theorem.** *If R is a dense ring of linear transformations of a vector space V such that every element of R has finite rank, then R is a simple ring.*

Proof: Let a be a nonzero element of R and let us show that $(a) = R$. By Theorem 7.4, there exists an element a' of R such that $a = aa'a$. Then $e = a'a$ is a nonzero idempotent of R, and hence e has finite nonzero rank. If b is an arbitrary nonzero element of R, Lemma 7.6 asserts that there exists an idempotent $h \in (e)$ which is a projection of V onto Vb. Thus for each $x \in V$ we have $xbh = xb$ and hence $bh = b$. Since $h \in (e)$ and $e \in (a)$, it follows that $h \in (a)$ and therefore also $b \in (a)$. This proves that $(a) = R$. Since the ideal generated by each nonzero element of R is the ring R, it follows that R is a simple ring.

The set F of all elements of finite rank of a dense ring R is an ideal in R (cf. 5.62, Exercise 2). The following corollary states several important properties of the ring F.

7.9   Corollary.   *Let R be a dense ring of linear transformations of a vector space V, and let F be the ideal in R consisting of all elements of R of finite rank. If $F \neq (0)$, then*

   (i) *F is a dense ring of linear transformations of the vector space V,*
   (ii) *F is a regular ring,*
   (iii) *F is a simple ring,*
   (iv) *F is contained in every nonzero ideal of R.*

The first three parts follow immediately from Theorems 7.7, 7.4, and 7.8. If K is a nonzero ideal in R, then as in the first part of the proof of Theorem 7.7 we have $VK = V$. Since $F \neq (0)$, we also have $VF = V$. Then $V(KF) = (VK)F = VF = V$, and $KF \neq (0)$. In particular, $K \cap F \neq (0)$ and since $K \cap F$ is an ideal in the simple ring F, we see that $K \cap F = F$ and $F \subseteq K$. This completes the proof of part (iv). Incidentally, part (iv) shows that R is a subdirectly irreducible ring.

We now pass to a further study of simple rings. Suppose that R is a simple ring such that $R^2 \neq (0)$ and such that R contains a maximal right ideal A (which is certainly the case if R has a unity). Since R is simple and $R^2 \neq (0)$, we must have $R^2 = R$ and therefore $R^2 \nsubseteq A$. We recall that

$$(A:R) = \{r \mid r \in R, Rr \subseteq A\}$$

and that $(A:R)$ is a two-sided ideal in R. Since $R^2 \nsubseteq A$, $(A:R) \neq R$ and therefore $(A:R) = (0)$. The first statement of the following theorem is thus implied by Theorems 5.32 and 5.44.

7.10   Theorem.   *Let R be a simple ring with $R^2 \neq (0)$ and such that R*

contains a maximal right ideal. Then R is isomorphic to a dense ring of linear transformations of a vector space over a division ring. Moreover, either all elements of R are of finite rank or R has no nonzero elements of finite rank.

Of course, when we speak of an element of R having finite rank we are referring to the rank of the linear transformation to which the element corresponds under the stated isomorphism.

The final statement of the theorem follows at once from the fact that the set of all elements of R of finite rank is an ideal in the simple ring R.

We next turn to a consideration of what it means for a dense ring to have a minimal right ideal. In this study an essential tool is the following result.

7.11   Lemma. *If A is a minimal right ideal in the arbitrary ring R such that $A^2 \neq (0)$, then there exists an idempotent e in A such that $A = eR$.*

Proof: Since $A^2 \neq (0)$, there exists $a \in A$ such that $aA \neq (0)$. But aA is a right ideal in R such that $aA \subseteq A$, and the minimality of A shows that $aA = A$. From this, it follows that there exists $e \in A$ such that $ae = a$ and clearly $e \neq 0$ since $a \neq 0$. Moreover, $ae^2 = ae$ or $a(e^2 - e) = 0$. If $B = \{c \mid c \in A, ac = 0\}$, B is a right ideal in R such that $B \subseteq A$ and $B \neq A$. Therefore we must have $B = (0)$. The equation $a(e^2 - e) = 0$ then implies that $e^2 = e$, and e is an idempotent element of A. Now $eR \subseteq A$ and $eR \neq (0)$ since eR contains $e^2 = e \neq 0$. Accordingly, $eR = A$ and the proof is completed.

7.12   Theorem. *Let R be a dense ring of linear transformations of a vector space V over a division ring D. Then R has nonzero elements of finite rank if and only if R contains a minimal right ideal.*

Proof: Suppose, first, that c is an element of R of finite rank $m > 0$. Then, by Theorem 7.4, there exists $c' \in R$ such that $c = cc'c$. If we set $e = c'c$, then e is an idempotent and it is easy to verify that $Vc = Ve$; hence e has rank $m > 0$. If y is a fixed nonzero element of V, Lemma 7.6 shows that there exists an idempotent f of R which is a projection of V onto yD. We shall prove that fR is a minimal right ideal of R by showing that if fa is an arbitrary nonzero element of fR, then $(fa)R = fR$.

If $yfa = 0$, then

$$V(fa) = (Vf)(fa) = (yD)(fa) = (yfa)D = 0.$$

However, $fa \neq 0$ and therefore $V(fa) \neq 0$, so we conclude that $yfa \neq 0$. Since R is dense, there exists $b \in R$ such that $yfab = y$. Since f is a projection of V onto yD, for each $x \in V$ we have $xf = y\alpha$ ($\alpha \in D$, depending on x). It follows that

$$xfab = (xf)(fab) = (y\alpha)(fab) = (yfab)\alpha = y\alpha = xf.$$

Therefore $fab = f$ and $fR \subseteq (fa)R$. Clearly, $(fa)R \subseteq fR$ and we conclude that $(fa)R = fR$. This shows that fR is a minimal right ideal in R and completes this part of the proof.

Suppose, now, that the dense ring R has a minimal right ideal A. Then, by 5.20, Exercise 7 (or by Corollary 6.8 and Theorem 6.16), we have $A^2 \neq (0)$. By Lemma 7.11, there exists an idempotent e in A such that $A = eR$. We shall prove that R has elements of nonzero finite rank by showing that the element e has rank 1. Since $e \neq 0$, $Ve \neq 0$. Let us assume that Ve has two linearly independent elements x_1 and x_2, and seek a contradiction. We have $x_1 e = x_1$, $x_2 e = x_2$. Moreover, the density of R assures the existence of an element a of R such that $x_1 a = 0$, $x_2 a = x_2$. Then $x_2 ea = x_2 a = x_2$, so $ea \neq 0$. The set $B = \{r \mid r \in A, \; x_1 r = 0\}$ is a right ideal of R contained in the minimal right ideal A, and $B \neq (0)$ since $ea \in B$. Hence $B = A$, and therefore $x_1 A = 0$. In particular, $x_1 e = 0$ and $x_1 = x_1 e = 0$. However, this contradicts the assumption that x_1 and x_2 are linearly independent. It follows that e has rank 1, and the proof is completed.

It is now easy to establish the following result.

7.13 Theorem. *Let R be a simple ring with $R^2 \neq (0)$ and having a minimal right ideal A. Then R is isomorphic to a dense ring of linear transformations of finite rank of a vector space over a division ring.*

Proof: Clearly, R is a prime ring and therefore $A^2 \neq (0)$ since $A \neq (0)$. It follows that A is not contained in the ideal $(0:A) = \{r \mid r \in R, \; Ar = 0\}$, and hence we must have $(0:A) = (0)$. Theorems 5.27 and 5.44 then show that R is isomorphic to a dense ring of linear transformations of some vector space. The preceding theorem asserts that R has non-zero elements of finite rank. Since R is simple, R must coincide with the ideal consisting of all elements of finite rank. This completes the proof of the theorem.

If T is the ring of *all* linear transformations of a vector space, an application of Corollary 7.9(iv) shows that every nonzero ideal in T contains the ideal consisting of all elements of T of finite rank. We conclude this section by proving the following rather special result to which we shall have occasion to refer in the following section.

7.14   Theorem.   *Let T be the ring of all linear transformations of a vector space V with a denumerable basis. Then the only proper ideal in T is the ideal F of all elements of T of finite rank.*

Proof: We shall assume it to be known that if the vector space V over a division ring D has one denumerable basis, every basis is denumerable and, moreover, every subspace of V of infinite dimension has a denumerable basis.

To prove the theorem we shall show that if $a \in T$, $a \notin F$, then $(a) = T$. By Theorem 7.3, there exists $a' \in T$ such that $a = aa'a$. If we set $e = a'a$, then e is idempotent, $Va = Ve$ and $(a) = (e)$. Accordingly, we only need to prove that if e is an idempotent of T such that the subspace Ve has infinite dimension, then $(e) = T$.

Since Ve is now assumed to have infinite dimension, it has a denumerable basis $X = \{x_1, x_2, \ldots\}$. Let us denote by V_e the null space of e, that is, the set of all vectors y of V such that $ye = 0$. Then V_e has a finite or denumerable basis Y. We now show that $X \cup Y$ is a basis of the entire space V. If $x \in V$, we may write $x = xe + (x - xe)$, where $xe \in Ve$ and $x - xe \in V_e$. Accordingly, V is generated by the set $X \cup Y$ and there remains only to prove that this set is linearly independent. Suppose that

$$\sum x_i \alpha_i + \sum y_j \beta_j = 0, \qquad \text{all } \alpha_i, \beta_j \in D,$$

the sums being finite, and the x_i and y_j being distinct elements of X and Y, respectively. Then, since $x_i e = x_i$ and $y_j e = 0$, we have

$$(\sum x_i \alpha_i + \sum y_j \beta_j)e = \sum x_i \alpha_i = 0,$$

and the linear independence of the set X shows that each $\alpha_i = 0$. Since now $\sum y_j \beta_j = 0$, the linear independence of the set Y shows that each $\beta_j = 0$. It follows that the set $X \cup Y$ is a linearly independent set and therefore a basis of V.

Let $Z = \{z_1, z_2, \ldots\}$ be a basis of V. It could be the basis we already have but it will simplify matters to have a new notation. Since there exists an element of T which maps the basis elements z_i $(i = 1, 2, \ldots)$ onto any specified elements of V, there exists an element d_1 of T such that

$$z_i d_1 = x_i, \qquad (i = 1, 2, \ldots).$$

In like manner, considering the basis $X \cup Y$, there exists an element d_2 of T (by no means unique) such that

$$x_i d_2 = z_i, \qquad (i = 1, 2, \ldots).$$

It follows that for each element z_i of the basis Z,

$$z_i d_1 e d_2 = x_i e d_2 = x_i d_2 = z_i, \qquad (i = 1, 2, \ldots).$$

We conclude that $d_1 e d_2$ is the unity of T, and $(e) = T$ as we wished to show. This completes the proof of the theorem.

37. ANOTHER RADICAL OF A RING

In this section we shall define still another radical of a ring and give a brief discussion of a few of its properties. Its relation to the Jacobson radical will be clarified if we first observe that the Jacobson radical $\mathfrak{J}(R)$ of a ring R can be characterized as follows:

7.15 $\qquad \mathfrak{J}(R) = \{b \mid b \in R, (b) \text{ is right quasi-regular}\}.$

This is an immediate consequence of Lemma 6.5 and Theorem 6.7. It will also be helpful to reformulate in the following obvious way the concept of right quasi-regularity. With each element a of R let us associate the right ideal $F(a)$ defined as follows:

$$F(a) = \{ar - r \mid r \in R\}.$$

Then a is right quasi-regular if and only if $a \in F(a)$.

If $a \in R$, let us now define $G(a)$ to be the two-sided ideal in R generated by the elements of the right ideal $F(a)$. We leave it as an exercise to verify that

7.16 $\qquad G(a) = \{ar - r + \sum(x_i a y_i - x_i y_i) \mid r, x_i, y_i \in R\},$

it being understood that all finite sums of the indicated form are to be included.

7.17 Definition. An element a of the ring R is said to be *G-regular* if $a \in G(a)$. An ideal is said to be *G-regular* if each of its elements is *G*-regular.

Since $F(a) \subseteq G(a)$, it is clear that if a is right quasi-regular, it is also *G*-regular. Moreover, for a *commutative* ring the two concepts coincide since in this case $F(a) = G(a)$.

7.18 Definition. The *radical* $\mathfrak{N}(R)$ of the ring R is defined as follows:

7.19 $$\mathfrak{N}(R) = \{b \mid b \in R, (b) \text{ is } G\text{-regular}\}.$$

It will be observed that this definition of $\mathfrak{N}(R)$ has the same form as the characterization 7.15 of $\mathfrak{J}(R)$ with "*G*-regular" replacing "right quasi-regular." Clearly, $\mathfrak{J}(R) \subseteq \mathfrak{N}(R)$, and they coincide in case R is a commutative ring.

It is not obvious from the definition that $\mathfrak{N}(R)$ is an ideal in R, but we shall prove that this is the case as soon as we have established the following useful result.

7.20 Lemma. *If $a - c$ is G-regular and $c \in G(a)$, then a is G-regular.*

Proof: If $a - c$ is *G*-regular, there exist elements r, x_i, y_i of R such that

$$a - c = (a - c)r - r + \sum [x_i(a - c)y_i - x_iy_i].$$

Hence we have

$$a = [ar - r + \sum (x_iay_i - x_iy_i)] + [c - cr - \sum x_icy_i].$$

Since $c \in G(a)$ and $G(a)$ is an ideal in R, the second of these bracketed terms is an element of $G(a)$. The first term also is an element of $G(a)$ and hence $a \in G(a)$, as we wished to show.

We shall now prove the following result.

7.21 Theorem. *The radical $\mathfrak{N}(R)$ of a ring R is an ideal in R.*

Proof: If $z \in \mathfrak{N}(R)$ and $t \in R$, then $(zt) \subseteq (z)$ and $(tz) \subseteq (z)$. Since (z)

is G-regular, it follows that (zt) and (tz) are G-regular, and therefore $zt \in \mathfrak{N}(R)$ and $tz \in \mathfrak{N}(R)$. There remains to prove that if z, $w \in \mathfrak{N}(R)$ and $a \in (z - w)$, then a is G-regular. Now $a = u - v$, for some $u \in (z)$ and $v \in (w)$. Since $z \in \mathfrak{N}(R)$, u is G-regular and there exist elements r, x_i, y_i of R such that

$$u = ur - r + \sum (x_i u y_i - x_i y_i).$$

If in this equation we replace u by $a + v$, we see that

$$a - [ar - r + \sum (x_i a y_i - x_i y_i)] = -v + vr + \sum x_i v y_i.$$

Since $v \in (w)$, the right member of this equation is an element of (w) and is therefore G-regular. Thus the left member is G-regular and, since the bracketed term is an element of $G(a)$, Lemma 7.20 shows that a is G-regular. This completes the proof of the theorem.

If R has a left unity e, then it is evident that $G(e) = (0)$ and e is not G-regular except in the trivial case in which R has only one element. In particular, if R is a simple ring with unity, $\mathfrak{N}(R) \neq R$ and therefore $\mathfrak{N}(R) = (0)$.

The following facts are frequently useful.

7.22 Lemma. *Let θ be a homomorphism of the ring R onto the ring S.*
    (i) *If $a \in R$, then $G(a\theta) = G(a)\theta$.*
    (ii) *If $a \in R$ such that a is G-regular, then $a\theta$ is G-regular.*
    (iii) *$\mathfrak{N}(R)\theta \subseteq \mathfrak{N}(S)$.*

We omit the proofs of the first two parts since they follow by straightforward calculations. To prove (iii), suppose that $b \in \mathfrak{N}(R)$ and that $a \in (b)$. Then a is G-regular and by part (ii), $a\theta$ is G-regular. Hence every element of $(b)\theta$ is G-regular. But 2.50, Exercise 5, shows that $(b)\theta = (b\theta)$. It follows that $(b\theta)$ is G-regular and hence that $b\theta \in \mathfrak{N}(S)$. We have therefore proved that $\mathfrak{N}(R)\theta \subseteq \mathfrak{N}(S)$, as we wished to show.

We shall next prove the following result.

7.23 Theorem. *If $\mathfrak{N}(R)$ is the radical of the ring R, it follows that $\mathfrak{N}(R/\mathfrak{N}(R)) = (0)$.*

Proof: Let θ denote the natural homomorphism of the ring R onto the ring $R/\mathfrak{N}(R)$, with kernel $\mathfrak{N}(R)$. Suppose that $b \in R$ such that $b\theta \in \mathfrak{N}(R/\mathfrak{N}(R))$. If $a \in (b)$, then $a\theta \in (b)\theta = (b\theta)$ and therefore $a\theta \in G(a\theta)$.

By Lemma 7.22(i), we then have $a\theta \in G(a)\theta$. Thus there exists $c \in G(a)$ such that $(a - c)\theta = 0$ and therefore $a - c \in \mathfrak{N}(R)$. It follows that $a - c$ is G-regular and Lemma 7.20 implies that a is G-regular. This shows that (b) is G-regular and it follows that $b \in \mathfrak{N}(R)$ and hence that $b\theta = 0$. The proof of the theorem is therefore completed.

The concept of modular right ideal played an important role in the study of the Jacobson radical. We now need the corresponding concept for two-sided ideals and we therefore make the following definition.

7.24 Definition.   An ideal K in a ring R is said to be a *modular ideal* if the ring R/K has a unity.

Of course, the ring R/K has a unity if and only if there exists an element e of R such that $er - r \in K$ and $re - r \in K$ for every $r \in R$. By a *modular maximal ideal* we shall mean a maximal ideal which is a modular ideal.

If R has a unity, every ideal in R is clearly modular. Moreover, in view of Corollary 2.46, an ideal M in R is a modular maximal ideal if and only if the ring R/M is a simple ring with unity. In this connection, the following lemma will be of some interest.

7.25 Lemma.   *If e is a left unity of a simple ring T, then T has e as unity.*

Proof: The set $E = \{xe - x \mid x \in T\}$ is easily seen to be an ideal in T. Suppose that $e \in E$ and therefore that $e = ye - y$ for some y in T. Right multiplication by e shows that $e = ye - ye = 0$, and it follows that $x = ex = 0$ for all x in T. However, our definition of a simple ring requires that it have more than one element. Hence $e \notin E$ and therefore $E \neq T$. Accordingly, we must have $E = (0)$, and hence e is a right unity and therefore the unity of T.

We next prove the following theorem.

7.26 Theorem.   *Let R be a ring such that $\mathfrak{N}(R) \neq R$, and let M_i, $i \in \mathfrak{A}$, be all the modular maximal ideals in R. Then*

$$\mathfrak{N}(R) = \bigcap_{i \in \mathfrak{A}} M_i.$$

Proof: We shall first show that $\cap M_i \subseteq \mathfrak{N}(R)$ by showing that if $b \notin \mathfrak{N}(R)$, then there exists a modular maximal ideal M such that

$b \notin M$. Now $b \notin \mathfrak{N}(R)$ implies that $a \notin G(a)$ for some $a \in (b)$. An application of Zorn's Lemma shows that there exists in R an ideal M which is maximal in the set of all those ideals which contain $G(a)$ but not the element a. We assert that M is actually a maximal ideal in R. For, suppose that M' is an ideal in R such that $M \subset M'$. Then we must have $a \in M'$. Since $G(a) \subseteq M'$ and $ar - r \in G(a)$ for all r in R, we conclude that $M' = R$. Hence M is a maximal ideal in R and since $ar - r \in M$ for all r in R, we know that the ring R/M is a simple ring with left unity $a + M$. Lemma 7.25 then shows that R/M is a simple ring with unity, and hence that M is a modular ideal. Since $a \notin M$ and $a \in (b)$, we must have $b \notin M$, and this part of the proof is completed.

Conversely, let M be an arbitrary modular maximal ideal in R. If $b \in \mathfrak{N}(R)$, then Lemma 7.22(iii) shows that $b + M$ is an element of $\mathfrak{N}(R/M)$. However, we pointed out preceding the statement of Lemma 7.22 that a simple ring with unity has zero radical. Accordingly, $b + M$ is the zero of R/M, that is, $b \in M$. Hence we must have $b \in \cap M_i$, and this completes the proof of the theorem.

The relation of the present radical to the concept of subdirect sum is pointed out in the next theorem.

7.27 Theorem. *If R is a ring with more than one element, then $\mathfrak{N}(R) = (0)$ if and only if R is isomorphic to a subdirect sum of simple rings with unity.*

Proof: If $\mathfrak{N}(R) = (0)$, then in the notation of the preceding theorem we have $\cap M_i = (0)$. Theorem 3.9 then shows that R is isomorphic to a subdirect sum of the rings R/M_i, and each such ring is a simple ring with unity. Conversely, suppose that R is isomorphic to a subdirect sum of simple rings S_i, $i \in \mathfrak{B}$, with unity. Since $\mathfrak{N}(S_i) = (0)$, Lemma 7.22(iii) shows that if ϕ_i is the natural homomorphism of R onto S_i (as defined in Section 13), then $\mathfrak{N}(R)\phi_i = (0)$, $i \in \mathfrak{B}$. However, this implies that $\mathfrak{N}(R) = (0)$, completing the proof.

We pointed out earlier that always $\mathfrak{J}(R) \subseteq \mathfrak{N}(R)$ and that equality holds for each *commutative* ring R. We now give an example in which equality does not hold. Let T be the ring of all linear transformations of a vector space V with a denumerable basis. Since T is a dense ring of linear transformations, and therefore a primitive ring, Theorem 6.16 shows that $\mathfrak{J}(T) = (0)$. Since T has a unity, $\mathfrak{N}(T) \neq T$. We know, by Theorem 7.14, that the only ideal in T besides (0) and T is the ideal F of all elements of T of finite rank. Since T is subdirectly irreducible and is not simple, it cannot be isomorphic to a subdirect sum of simple rings with unity, and the preceding theorem shows that $\mathfrak{N}(T) \neq (0)$. Accordingly, we must have $\mathfrak{N}(T) = F$. For this ring T we therefore have $\mathfrak{J}(T) \subset \mathfrak{N}(T)$.

We proved in Corollary 6.26 that in the presence of the d.c.c. for right ideals in R, the Jacobson radical $\mathfrak{J}(R)$ coincides with the prime radical $\mathfrak{P}(R)$. We conclude our discussion of the radical $\mathfrak{N}(R)$ by completing the proof of the following theorem.

7.28 Theorem. *If the d.c.c. for right ideals holds in the ring R, then* $\mathfrak{N}(R) = \mathfrak{J}(R) = \mathfrak{P}(R)$.

There only remains to prove that $\mathfrak{N}(R) \subseteq \mathfrak{J}(R)$. If the d.c.c. for right ideals holds in the ring R, it also holds in the homomorphic image $R/\mathfrak{J}(R)$ of R. Moreover, we know by Theorem 6.9 that the ring $R/\mathfrak{J}(R)$ has zero Jacobson radical. By the Wedderburn–Artin Theorem (5.59), $R/\mathfrak{J}(R)$ is isomorphic to a direct sum of rings each of which is a complete matrix ring over a division ring. Each of these component rings is simple (by Corollary 2.28) and has a unity. Accordingly, Theorem 7.27 shows that $\mathfrak{N}(R/\mathfrak{J}(R)) = (0)$. It follows, by Lemma 7.22(iii) that $\mathfrak{N}(R)$ maps into the zero ideal under the natural homomorphism of R onto $R/\mathfrak{J}(R)$. This implies that $\mathfrak{N}(R) \subseteq \mathfrak{J}(R)$, and the proof is completed.

The radical $\mathfrak{N}(R)$ has several other properties which, like most of those that have been proved here, are close analogues of corresponding properties of the radicals $\mathfrak{P}(R)$ and $\mathfrak{J}(R)$. The interested reader may find these properties in references which will be given in the notes to this chapter. We shall also give references to some additional definitions of the radical of a ring.

7.29 EXERCISES

1. If R is a regular ring, prove that $\mathfrak{J}(R) = (0)$.
2. Show that if R is a ring such that $\mathfrak{J}(R) = (0)$ and the d.c.c. for right ideals holds in R, then R is a regular ring.
3. Prove Formula 7.16.
4. Prove the first two parts of Lemma 7.22.
5. Prove that if $\mathfrak{J}(R) = (0)$, then R is a subring of a regular ring.
6. Let R be a simple ring with $R^2 \neq (0)$ and such that the d.c.c. for right ideals does not hold in R. Prove that if R has a minimal right ideal, then R cannot have a unity.

7. If R is a simple ring, prove that $\mathfrak{N}(R) = R$ if and only if R does not have a unity.

8. In the notation of Theorem 7.14, show that $\mathfrak{I}(F) = (0)$ and that $\mathfrak{N}(F) = F$. Show also that $\mathfrak{I}(T/F) = \mathfrak{N}(T/F) = (0)$.

9. In the notation of the proof of Theorem 7.3, let us add to the definition of a' the further requirement that $za' = 0$ for each z in Z. Show that for such an element a' not only is $aa'a = a$ but also $a'aa' = a'$.

Notes

THESE NOTES are of a rather miscellaneous and informal nature. Some of them indicate original source references for specific theorems or concepts, others offer suggestions for further reading. Moreover, we give hints for the solutions (and in some cases complete solutions) of selected exercises. These are primarily the exercises which are somewhat tricky or those which form an essential part of the theory and to which reference will be made at a later point in the text.

Numbers in square brackets refer to the list of references immediately following these notes. We have included only those items to which we have occasion to refer, and have made no attempt to give a comprehensive bibliography on ring theory. For this reason, it may well happen that the most important papers of a particular author do not appear on our list and, for that matter, a number of important contributors to the subject are not even mentioned. A fairly extensive bibliography (up to 1955 or 1956) will be found in Jacobson [7].

CHAPTER I

Introductions to ring theory will be found in Jacobson [5], McCoy [3], Miller [1], Moore [1], van der Waerden [1], and (for commutative rings) Zariski and Samuel [1].

Section 1. Proofs that any integral domain can be imbedded in a field of quotients will be found in the general references given above as well as in many other texts. Actually, a somewhat more general result is of importance for some purposes. Let M be a *multiplicative system* in a commutative ring R, that is, a nonempty set of elements of R which is closed under the operation of multiplication. Suppose, further, that no element of M is a divisor of zero. Then R can be imbedded in a ring of quotients a/b, where $a \in R$ and $b \in M$, and in this ring every element of M has a multiplicative inverse. For details, see Zariski and Samuel [1] or McCoy [3]. The commutativity of R is essential in this construction. Ore [1] gives conditions under which such a ring of quotients can be constructed in the noncommutative case. In this connection, Malcev [1] has given an example of a ring, necessarily noncommutative, which has no nonzero divisors of zero but which cannot be a subring of any division ring.

Readers who have previously seen polynomial rings $R[x]$ introduced by starting with a new symbol or indeterminate x may be interested in a different approach in terms of sequences of elements of R. See Jacobson [5], p. 94 or Zariski and Samuel [1], p. 24.

For references to the ring of all subsets of a given set, we may refer to the note at the end of the first chapter of McCoy [3].

Section 2. Some variations and generalizations of this imbedding process are given in Brown and McCoy [1].

Frequently, when we have a ring R which is isomorphic to a subring of a ring S, we find it convenient to consider that R is actually a subring of S. For the ideas involved in justifying this procedure, see Zariski and Samuel [1], p. 19.

1.13 Exercises

12. If $xm + yn = 1$, then $(xm)^2 \equiv xm$ (mod mn) and $(yn)^2 \equiv yn$ (mod mn).

16. If e is a left unity and $a \in R$, then $e + ae - a$ also is a left unity.

18. If $b^2 = 0$, then $(a + b)^{-1} = a^{-1} - a^{-2}b$; if $b^3 = 0$, then $(a + b)^{-1} = a^{-1} - a^{-2}b + a^{-3}b^2$. Generalize.

23. Consider $(ex - exe)^2$ and $(xe - exe)^2$.

25. As to notation, we are here using i^* to designate the residue class (equivalence set) modulo n which contains the integer i. By *well-defined*, we mean "not dependent on the notation." That is, if $(a_1, i_1^*) = (a_2, i_2^*)$ and $(b_1, j_1^*) = (b_2, j_2^*)$, then $(a_1, i_1^*)(b_1, j_1^*) = (a_2, i_2^*)(b_2, j_2^*)$.

26. (i) If $a = aba$ and $ac = 0$ or $ca = 0$, then $a = a(b + c)a$.

Section 3. Algebras are sometimes called linear algebras, linear associative algebras or hypercomplex numbers. An introduction to this concept, with at least some material on the algebra of matrices, will be found in many texts such as, for example, Birkhoff and MacLane [1], Macduffee [1]. For some deeper results and an extensive bibliography, see Albert [1].

Quaternions were introduced in 1843 by Sir William R. Hamilton. From an historical point of view, the significance of his achievement lies not so much in the importance of the system itself (although for a time quaternions were considered to be very important as a tool in geometry, physics, etc.) as in the fact that algebra was thereby freed from the commutativity of multiplication as a necessary assumption. Macduffee [1] presents quaternions in some detail and also gives some other examples of division rings. We may remark that there is a famous theorem of Wedderburn [1] which asserts that a division ring with a finite number of elements is necessarily a field. Many different proofs have been given of this fact, the latest and perhaps the most elementary by Herstein [1].

Section 4.   For a discussion of formal power series in any finite number of indeterminates (particularly, in the commutative case), see Zariski and Samuel [2], p. 129 ff.

Section 5.   The terminology of infinite direct sums is not standardized in the literature, so the definitions should be checked in every case. For example, our *discrete direct sum* is sometimes called a *weak direct sum* or simply a *direct sum*.

1.35   Exercises

7. An element is in the center if and only if it commutes with i, j, and k.
8. An element is in the center if and only if it commutes with every matrix unit E_{ij}.

CHAPTER 2

General references for this chapter are Jacobson [5], McCoy [3], van der Waerden [1] and [2], Zariski and Samuel [1].

Sections 6 and 7.   Several of the concepts of this chapter can be developed in a more general setting as follows.

Let us say that a set P is a *partially ordered set* if a relation $\prec$ is defined on certain, but not necessarily all, ordered pairs of elements of P such that the following are true:

   (i) $a \prec a$ for each $a \in P$.
   (ii) If a, $b \in P$ such that $a \prec b$ and $b \prec a$, then $a = b$.
   (iii) If a, b, $c \in P$ such that $a \prec b$ and $b \prec c$, then $a \prec c$.

We may emphasize that if a and b are elements of the partially ordered set P, it may very well be true that *no* one of the following holds: $a \prec b$, $b \prec a$, $a = b$.

Now let X be a subset of the partially ordered set P. An element c of P is an *upper bound* of the set X if $x \prec c$ for every element x of X. Moreover, c is the *least upper bound* (l.u.b.) of X if c is an upper bound of X and $c \prec c_1$ for every upper bound c_1 of X. Analogous definitions hold for *lower bound* and *greatest lower bound* (g.l.b.).

A partially ordered set P is called a *lattice* if each subset $\{a, b\}$, where $a, b \in P$, has a l.u.b. and a g.l.b. in P.

One interesting example of a lattice is the set of all subsets of a given set S with the partial order being set inclusion. That is, if a and b are subsets of S, we define $a \prec b$ to mean $a \subseteq b$. Then $a \cup b$ is the l.u.b. and $a \cap b$ the g.l.b. of $\{a, b\}$.

For our present purposes, a more important observation is that the set of all right ideals (or ideals, or left ideals) in a given ring R is a lattice L with respect to the partial ordering given by set inclusion. If $A, B \in L$, then the l.u.b. of $\{A, B\}$ is $A + B$, and the g.l.b. is $A \cap B$. Moreover, the l.u.b. of any set of elements of L (that is, of right ideals in R) is their sum or join, and the g.l.b. is their intersection. This particular lattice has an important property, not true in all lattices, which will be stated as 2.18, Exercise 11.

The basic reference to partially ordered sets and lattices is Birkhoff [2].

2.9 Exercises

15. (Theorem 2.8(iii)) Suppose that A is a nonzero ideal in $F[[x]]$, and let k be the smallest nonnegative integer such that A contains an element of the form $f(x) = a_k x^k + a_{k+1} x^{k+1} + \cdots$, with $a_k \neq 0$. Then $f(x) = x^k(a_k + a_{k+1} x + \cdots)$ and the second factor has an inverse by Lemma 1.29. Hence $x^k \in A$. Show now that $A = (x^k)$.

17. An elementary proof is given in McCoy [3], p. 19.

18. Suppose that $f(x) = a_0 + a_1 x + \cdots + a_n x^n$ of degree $n > 0$ has $g(x) = b_0 + b_1 x + \cdots + b_m x^m$ of degree $m \geq 0$ as inverse. Let $k \leq n$ be a positive integer such that every coefficient a_i of $f(x)$ with $i > k$ is nilpotent, and let us show that a_k is nilpotent. By considering the coefficients of $x^{k+m}, \ldots, x^k$ in $f(x)g(x) = 1$, we find that each of the following is an element of the ideal N of all nilpotent elements of R (cf. 2.9, Exercise 4):

$$a_k b_m,$$
$$a_k b_{m-1} + a_{k-1} b_m,$$
$$\cdot \quad \cdot \quad \cdot \quad \cdot \quad \cdot \quad \cdot$$
$$a_k b_0 + a_{k-1} b_1 + \cdots.$$

If we multiply the second of these expressions by a_k and use the fact that

$a_k b_m \in N$, we conclude that $a_k^2 b_{m-1} \in N$. Similarly, by multiplying the third expression by a_k^2, we find that $a_k^3 b_{m-2} \in N$. A continuation of this procedure shows that $a_k^{m+1} b_0 \in N$. Since b_0 has an inverse in R, it follows that $a_k^{m+1} \in N$ and therefore that $a_k \in N$.

2.18 Exercises

4. Suppose that $f(x) = a_0 + a_1 x + \cdots + a_n x^n$ is nilpotent. Then a_0 is nilpotent (why?). If $a_0, a_1, \ldots, a_k$ are nilpotent, then $f(x) - (a_0 + a_1 x + \cdots + a_k x^k) = x^{k+1}(a_{k+1} + \cdots)$ is nilpotent, and it follows that a_{k+1} is nilpotent.

11. This is Dedekind's "modular law" (Birkhoff [2], p. 65). We prove inclusion one way. Suppose that e is an element of $(A + B) \cap C$. Then $e \in C$ and $e = a + b$, with $a \in A$ and $b \in B$. Since $A \subseteq C$, we have $a \in C$ and therefore $b = e - a \in C$. Therefore, $b \in (B \cap C)$ and $e = a + b$ is an element of $A + (B \cap C)$.

13. The only possibly tricky point is in proving that multiplication is preserved under the given mapping. If $b \in A_i$ and $c \in A_j$, with $i \neq j$, then $bc \in (A_i \cap A_j) = (0)$. Therefore

$$(a_1 + a_2 + \cdots + a_n)(b_1 + b_2 + \cdots + b_n) = a_1 b_1 + a_2 b_2 + \cdots + a_n b_n.$$

Section 9. These conditions can easily be formulated for partially ordered sets in general. For example, let X be a subset of a partially ordered set P. Then a is a *minimal element* of X if $a \in X$ and $x \prec a$ with $x \in X$ implies that $x = a$. Similarly, a *maximal element* of X is defined. The special case in which we are here interested is the partially ordered set consisting of all ideals in a given ring R, as defined in the notes to Sections 6 and 7. A minimal ideal in R is then a minimal element of the set consisting of all nonzero ideals in R, and a maximal ideal in R is a maximal element of the set consisting of all ideals in R other than R itself.

A comprehensive study of rings in which the d.c.c. for right ideals holds is Artin, Nesbitt and Thrall [1]. Incidentally, "minimum condition" means the same as the d.c.c. (See note to 2.29, Exercise 8 below.)

It is also true that if the a.c.c. for right ideals holds in a ring R, then every nil right ideal in R is nilpotent. This result is due to Levitzki. See Utumi [1] and other references there given.

2.29 Exercises

8. If the condition here stated holds, the *minimum condition* for right ideals is said to hold in R. Suppose, first, that this condition holds and that $A_1, A_2, \ldots$ are right ideals in R such that $A_1 \supset A_2 \supset \cdots$. The minimum condition assures us that the set $\{A_1, A_2, \ldots\}$ contains a minimal element, say A_n. Then the set has only n elements and the d.c.c. therefore holds. Conversely, suppose that the d.c.c. for right ideals holds, and let S be a nonempty set of right ideals in R. Choose $A_1 \in S$. If A_1 is not a minimal element of S, there exists $A_2 \in S$ such that $A_1 \supset A_2$. If A_2 is not a minimal element of S, there exists $A_3 \in S$ such that $A_1 \supset A_2 \supset A_3$. In view of the d.c.c. this process must come to an end in a finite number of steps and S therefore has a minimal element.

9. Show that if a is a nonzero element of R, then $aR \neq (0)$. Then apply 2.9, Exercise 17.

10. Suppose that $R^2 = (0)$. Then R is just an abelian group with operation addition, and it must be generated by every nonzero element. Hence R is a finite cyclic group of prime order.

11. Let B be a nonzero right ideal such that $B \subseteq rA$. Use the minimal property of A to show that $\{a \mid a \in A, ra \in B\} = A$; hence that $rA \subseteq B$.

12. The sum of all minimal right ideals in R is called the *right socle* of R. Naturally, the *left socle* is defined similarly. These concepts were introduced and studied by Dieudonné [1]. See also Jacobson [7], p. 64. It is known that the right socle and the left socle of R coincide if R contains no nonzero nilpotent ideals.

2.36   Exercises

7. Use the mapping $\sum (r_{ij} + A)E_{ij} \rightarrow (\sum r_{ij}E_{ij}) + A_n$.

10. If $R' = \{(a, 0) \mid a \in R\}$, then $R \cong R'$. (ii) Show that $R' \cap A$ is the zero of T, then use Exercise 6. (iii) Show that if $(a, n)(b, m) \in A$ with $(b, m) \notin A$, then $(a, n) \in A$. In the calculations, remember that R has no unity!

2.50   Exercises

5. Each element of $(a)_r$ is of the form $na + at$, $n \in I$, $t \in R$. Moreover, $[na + at]\theta = n[a\theta] + [a\theta][t\theta]$, which is an element of $(a\theta)_r$. Hence $(a)_r\theta \subseteq (a\theta)_r$. Similarly, prove that $(a\theta)_r \subseteq (a)_r\theta$. For the last statement of the exercise, if U is a right ideal in S, then $U\theta^{-1}$ is a principal right ideal $(a)_r$ in R. Then $U = (U\theta^{-1})\theta = (a)_r\theta = (a\theta)_r$. Similarly for ideals instead of right ideals.

7. (iii) $[(U + V)\theta^{-1}]\theta = U + V$ and, by part (i), $(U\theta^{-1} + V\theta^{-1})\theta = (U\theta^{-1})\theta + (V\theta^{-1})\theta = U + V$. Thus, by Theorem 2.45(iv), we must have $(U + V)\theta^{-1} = U\theta^{-1} + V\theta^{-1}$.

(iv) Let $a \in U\theta^{-1}$ and $b \in V\theta^{-1}$, so that $a\theta \in U$ and $b\theta \in V$. Then $(ab)\theta = (a\theta)(b\theta) \in UV$, and $ab \in (UV)\theta^{-1}$. Since every element of $(U\theta^{-1})(V\theta^{-1})$ is a sum of such terms ab, we obtain the desired result. [It is easy to show by examples, even with $U = V = (0)$, that *equality* need not hold.]

8. Every decreasing chain of right ideals in S is of the form $U_1\theta \supset U_2\theta \supset \cdots$, where $U_1 \supset U_2 \supset \cdots$ is a chain of right ideals in R.

11. Let θ be the natural homomorphism of R onto R/N, with kernel N. If U is a nil ideal in R/N, show that $U\theta^{-1}$ is a nil ideal in R. Hence $U\theta^{-1} \subseteq N$ and $U = (U\theta^{-1})\theta = (0)$.

13. Use Theorem 2.8(iii) and show that $F[[x]]/(x^k) \cong F[x]/(x^k)$.

14. If $a \in A$, $b \in B$, show that the mapping $a + b \to a + (A \cap B)$ is (i) a well-defined mapping of $A + B$ onto $A/(A \cap B)$, (ii) that it is a homomorphism, and (iii) that its kernel is B. Then apply the Fundamental Theorem on Homomorphisms.

15. The set $\{a \mid a \in A, ra = 0\}$ is a right ideal of R which is contained in A and is not equal to A. Hence it is (0). The mapping $\theta : a \to a\theta = ra$, $a \in A$, is then an R-isomorphism of A onto rA.

16. This result and various related ones are due to Dieudonné [1].

CHAPTER 3

Birkhoff [1] pointed out, for general algebraic systems, the significance of the principal concept of this chapter. An exposition of the material presented here, together with references, will be found in McCoy [2].

Section 13. Theorem 3.6 was formulated in essentially this form in McCoy and Montgomery [1] but it is implicit in earlier results of other authors, as indicated in references in the paper just mentioned and in McCoy [2].

Section 14. Zorn's Lemma may be formulated in the more general setting of partially ordered sets as introduced in notes to Sections 6 and 7. Let us call a subset Q of a partially ordered set P a *chain* (also called a *simply* ordered set or a *totally* ordered set) if for a, $b \in Q$ it is always true that $a \prec b$ or $b \prec a$. Making use of the concept of maximal element (see notes to Section 9), we may formulate Zorn's Lemma as follows.

Zorn's Lemma. *If a partially ordered set P has the property that every chain in P has an upper bound in P, then P contains one or more maximal elements.*

What we called Zorn's Lemma (3.10) in the text is the special case in which $\mathfrak{M}$ is considered to be partially ordered by set inclusion. Of course, the union of the elements of a chain is in this case not only an upper bound but in fact the least upper bound.

A discussion of Zorn's Lemma and related concepts, along with references, will be found in Birkhoff [2], p. 42.

Section 15. Theorems 3.13 and 3.14 are due to Birkhoff [1]. The subdirectly irreducible commutative rings were characterized in McCoy [1]. See also Divinsky [1].

3.15 Exercises

1. (i) If $b_k \in B\theta_k$, there exists some element $(\ldots, b_k, \ldots)$ of B with k^{th} component b_k. Then

$$(\ldots, b_k, \ldots)(0, \ldots, 0, 1, 0, \ldots, 0) = (0, \ldots, 0, b_k, 0, \ldots, 0) \in B.$$

8. Every homomorphic image of R has the same property. Then use Theorem 3.13 and the result of the preceding exercise.

Rings with the property stated as the hypothesis in this exercise have been studied extensively. Jacobson proved that any such ring is necessarily commutative, and this result has been generalized in various ways. See Jacobson [7], p. 217ff. An elementary proof will be found in Herstein [1].

Section 16. Boolean rings were introduced and studied extensively by Stone [1].

3.21 Exercises

1. These rings were introduced in McCoy and Montgomery [1], where commutativity was assumed as in the statement of this exercise. However, the remarks to 3.15, Exercise 8, show that commutativity is a necessary consequence of the assumption that $a^p = a$ for each element a of R. An elementary proof for this particular case will be found in McCoy [3].

CHAPTER 4

The basic results about prime ideals in arbitrary *commutative* rings are largely due to Krull [1], and an exposition of some of them is found in McCoy [3]. An extension to general rings, along the lines of the present chapter, was begun in McCoy [4]. Other references to specific results will be given below.

4.9 Exercises

8. If $a, b \in R$ such that $aRb \subseteq (P \cap R)$, then $aR[x]bR[x] \subseteq P$.

9. Let $a, b \in A$ such that $aAb \subseteq (A \cap P)$. Then $aRbRb \subseteq aAb \subseteq P$ and therefore $aRbRbR \subseteq P$ and Theorem 4.3(iv) shows that $aR \subseteq P$ or $bR \subseteq P$. Show that then $a \in P$ or $b \in P$.

10. Let M be a maximal ideal, A and B ideals such that $A \nsubseteq M$ and $B \nsubseteq M$. Then $M + A = R$, $M + B = R$, and $(M + A)(M + B) = R$. Hence $AB \nsubseteq M$ since, otherwise, we would have $M = R$.

11. (i) Let $P \supseteq K$ be a prime ideal in R. By Theorem 2.45(iv), every ideal in S is of the form $A\theta$, where A is an ideal in R which contains K. Suppose that $(A\theta)(B\theta) \subseteq P\theta$. Then, by 2.50, Exercise 7(ii), $(AB)\theta \subseteq P\theta$ and $AB \subseteq P$ (why?). Hence $A \subseteq P$ or $B \subseteq P$ and, finally, $A\theta \subseteq P\theta$ or $B\theta \subseteq P\theta$.

Sections 19 and 20. The fact that certain fundamental properties of semi-prime ideals parallel those of prime ideals, with n-systems taking the place of m-systems, is suggested by the approach in Brown and McCoy [6].

Baer [1] introduced the *lower radical* of a ring R as the intersection of all ideals A such that the ring R/A has no nonzero nilpotent right ideals, and he proved that the lower radical is a nil ideal. In our present language, the lower radical is the intersection of all semi-prime ideals in R. The fact that the lower radical coincides with the prime radical was proved independently by Levitzki [2] and Nagata [1]. Nagata's elegant proof was the inspiration for our Lemma 4.14, which furnishes the essential part of the proof of Theorem 4.15.

Nagata [1] also introduced the now widely accepted term *semi-prime* ring for a ring with zero prime radical. In view of Theorem 4.25, a semi-prime ring is one that contains no nonzero nilpotent ideals. See, for example, Johnson [2] for a study of certain properties of these rings.

Another simple property of the prime radical (which is either not always true or at least not known to be true of the other radicals to be introduced in Chapters 6 and 7) is the following. If $R[x]$ is the ring of polynomials in an indeterminate x over R, then $\mathfrak{P}(R[x]) = (\mathfrak{P}(R))[x]$. Independent proofs of this fact will be found in Amitsur [4] and McCoy [5].

4.18 Exercises

3. Let S be the given set. Show that S and A are contained in the same semi-prime ideals by an argument similar to that following Definition 4.5. Then apply arguments similar to those used in the proof of Theorem 4.7 with m-systems replaced by n-systems.

Section 21. Some fundamental results on the structure of prime rings have been obtained by Johnson [1]. Among other more recent papers we may mention Goldie [1].

Section 22. Theorem 4.30 is a result of Hopkins [1], but the present proof is due to R. Brauer. See Jacobson [1], p. 64.

CHAPTER 5

General references for most of the material of this chapter are the various books [1], [5], [6], and [7] of Jacobson. Specific references to these, and to other sources, will be given at certain points in the notes below.

Sections 23 and 24.   In Definition 5.1 we could have used the notation ax, instead of xa, for the image of x under the mapping a. Had we done this, our definition of the product ab of two endomorphisms would have been as follows: $(ab)x = a(bx)$. That is, ab would have been the result of *first* applying the mapping b and then the mapping a. In this notation, the ring of all endomorphisms of V would have its products reversed, that is, it would be anti-isomorphic (5.20, Exercise 4) to the ring Δ of the text.

A primitive ring (Definition 5.19) could more accurately be called a *right primitive* ring. A ring would be *left primitive* if it were anti-isomorphic to an irreducible ring of endomorphisms of some abelian group (as defined in the text). It is an unsolved problem whether there exists a ring which is right primitive but not left primitive, or vice versa.

5.20   Exercises

6. Let a be a nonzero element of the commutative primitive ring R. There exists $x \in V$ such that $xa \neq 0$. Hence $(xa)R = V$ and also $xR = V$. Thus there exists $c \in R$ such that $(xa)c = x$. Show that for every element xr of V, $(xr)(ac) = xr$; hence that c is the inverse of a.

7. If A and B are ideals such that $AB = (0)$ and $A \neq (0)$, then $VA = V$ and $V(AB) = VB = 0$.

Section 25.   In an R-module, as here defined, the elements of R are written on the right; hence it could be more precisely called a *right* R-module. Of course, left modules can be similarly defined, but the notation we have introduced for endomorphisms makes right R-modules the appropriate ones for our purposes.

We may briefly explain some of the terminology which is not used here but which appears in Jacobson [7], the basic reference to the structure of rings. A *representation* of a ring R is a homomorphism of R onto a ring of endomorphisms of an abelian group. A representation is *faithful* if the homomorphism is an isomorphism. An R-module leads in a natural way (Theorem 5.26) to a representation of R. Conversely, a representation of R yields an R-module (Jacobson [7], p. 1), so the study of representations essentially coincides with the study of R-modules. An R-module M is said to be *irreducible* if $MR \neq \{0\}$ and the only R-submodules of M are the trivial ones, namely, the zero submodule and M itself. If M is a faithful irreducible R-module, then R is isomorphic to an irreducible ring of endomorphisms of M considered as an abelian group. The converse of this is also true, so that a primitive ring can be *defined* as a ring for which there exists a faithful irreducible R-module. (Historically, the term was first used in Jacobson [3], where a ring R was defined to be a primitive ring if it contains a maximal right ideal A such that $(A:R) = (0)$. Cf. Theorems 5.32 and 5.34.)

Section 26. Vector spaces over division rings are discussed most thoroughly in Jacobson [6].

Sections 27–30. The basic reference for most of this material is Jacobson [7], where many other related results are also given. The important Density Theorem (5.44) and a number of its applications first appeared in Jacobson [2]. Our proof of this theorem is taken from mimeographed notes of Kaplansky. As indicated by Kaplansky, it is essentially the proof of Artin [2].

Wedderburn [2] first proved the so-called Wedderburn–Artin Theorem (5.59) for algebras of finite dimension over a field, and Artin [1] extended it to rings in which both the d.c.c. and the a.c.c. for left ideals holds. Hopkins [1] proved that it was sufficient to assume the presence of the d.c.c. only. See van der Waerden [2] for an exposition of the theory using only the d.c.c.

A most illuminating account of several of the results here presented, including the Density Theorem and the Wedderburn–Artin Theorem, will be found in Artin [2].

5.62 Exercises

2. (i) $V(ca) = (Vc)a \subseteq Va$, so the rank of ca cannot exceed the rank of a. If $\{x_1a, \ldots, x_na\}$ is a basis of Va, then each x in Va is a linear combination of $\{x_1a, \ldots, x_na\}$; and $V(ac)$ is generated by $\{x_1ac, \ldots, x_nac\}$. Thus the dimension of $V(ac)$ cannot exceed n.

3. For example, a linear transformation c which maps every basis element onto the same nonzero element of V is such that $c \in T$, $c \notin K$.

4, 5. Apply the Wedderburn–Artin Theorem.

CHAPTER 6

The concept of quasi-regularity was introduced by Perlis [1] who showed that it could be used to give an interesting characterization of the radical of an algebra of finite dimension over a field. Baer [1] showed that in an arbitrary ring the sum of all right quasi-regular right ideals is a right ideal, and established some of its properties. However, the central importance of this concept in the structure theory of arbitrary rings was first pointed out in a classic paper of Jacobson [3]. A most complete exposition of the Jacobson radical and related results will be found in Jacobson [7]. The *definition* of the radical given there is in terms of the concept of irreducible module and is equivalent to using as definition the property which we have expressed in Theorem 6.21.

6.27 Exercises

3. If R has a unity 1, then $1 - a^n = (1 - a)(1 + a + \cdots + a^{n-1})$. Hence if $1 - b$ is a right inverse of $1 - a^n$, then $(1 + a + \cdots + a^{n-1})(1-b)$ is a right inverse of $1 - a$. These ideas lead to the following: If $a^n \circ b = 0$, then $a \circ \left[\left(- \sum_{i=1}^{n-1} a^i \right) \circ b \right] = 0$.

6. Clearly, $eJ(R)e \subseteq J(R)$, so each element of $eJ(R)e$ has a q.i. in R; show that its q.i. is in eRe, and hence that $eJ(R)e \subseteq J(eRe)$. Conversely, if $eae \in J(eRe)$, then $eae(eRe)$ is r.q.r. in eRe, that is, $eaexe$ is r.q.r. for every x in R. By Lemma 6.4, $eaex$ is r.q.r. and this implies that $eae \in J(R)$. Then $eae \in eJ(R)e$, so $J(eRe) \subseteq eJ(R)e$. (For some related results, see Jacobson [7], p. 48.)

7. If θ is the natural homomorphism of R onto R/K with kernel K, then (by Lemma 6.13) $J(R)\theta = J(R)/K \subseteq J(R\theta) = J(R/K)$. Conversely, if $a + K \in J(R/K)$, then $(a + K)(x + K) = ax + K$ is r.q.r. for every x in R, and thus there exists y in R such that $(ax) \circ y \in K \subseteq J$. It follows that $(ax) \circ y$ is r.q.r. in R and therefore that ax is r.q.r. in R. Since this is true for every x in R, we conclude that $a \in J(R)$ and hence that $a + K \in J(R)/K$.

10. Since R is an ideal in S, Theorem 6.14 shows that $J(R) = R \cap J(S)$. If $(a, n) \in J(S)$, verify that $n \in J(I) = (0)$.

11. See Jacobson [7], p. 21 for this result and some applications.

12. A result of Kaplansky states that if an element of a ring has more than one right inverse, it has an infinite number of right inverses. For a simple proof, see Bitzer [1]. See also Jacobson [4].

CHAPTER 7

Sections 35 and 36. Theorems 7.3, 7.4, and 7.14 are due to Johnson and Kiokemeister [1]. A generalized form of Theorem 7.14 is given in Jacobson [6]. Most of the other results of these sections (except for the well-known Lemma 7.11) were obtained by Jacobson [2]. See also Jacobson [7].

Regular rings were introduced and studied by von Neumann [1]. Corollary 7.5 is a special case of von Neumann's result that if R is a regular ring, then the complete matrix ring R_n is regular. A simple proof of this fact is given in Brown and McCoy [4]. The significance of the concept of regular element (Definition 7.2) for matrix rings over a division ring was pointed out by E. H. Moore in his *General Analysis*, Part I, 1935, pp. 197–209. This reference to Moore's work is given in mimeographed notes of von Neumann of 1936–1937.

We now make a few remarks about Theorem 7.7. Suppose that K is a nonzero ideal in a dense ring R of linear transformations of a vector space V over a division ring D. By Theorem 5.18, K is an irreducible ring of endomorphisms of V considered as an abelian group, and the Density Theorem (5.44) assures us that K is a dense ring of linear transformations of V considered as a vector space over the centralizer of K in the ring Δ of all endomorphisms of V. Theorem 5.47 states that the centralizer of R in Δ is D. We now show directly that the centralizer of K in Δ coincides with the centralizer of R in Δ, and this gives another proof of Theorem 7.7. Suppose that a is a nonzero element of the centralizer of K in Δ. Since $K \subseteq R$, we can complete the proof by showing that a is also in the centralizer of R. If $r \in R$ and $k \in K$, then $rk \in K$ and so a commutes with rk as well as with k. For each x in V, we then have

$$xark = xrka = xrak,$$

and hence $x(ar - ra)K = 0$. But since K is an irreducible ring of endomorphisms of V, this implies that $x(ar - ra) = 0$. Hence $ar = ra$, and a is indeed in the centralizer of R in Δ.

The properties of a basis which are stated in the first paragraph of the proof of Theorem 7.14 are proved (more generally) in Jacobson [6], p. 240.

Section 37. Most of the material of this section is taken from Brown and McCoy [2] and [3]. This radical (for group algebras) was introduced independently by Segal [1], using as definition the property stated in Theorem 7.26.

In addition to the three radicals of a ring which have been introduced in this book, a number of other radicals have been studied from various points of view. As references, we may mention Baer [1], Brown and McCoy [2] and [5], Levitzki [1], and Amitsur [1], [2], and [3]. Many of the concepts of radical of a ring have also been extended to more general algebraic systems. For the case of nonassociative rings (that is, systems which satisfy all the ring properties except possibly the associative law of multiplication) the Jacobson radical has been studied by Brown [1]; the prime radical by Behrens [1] and Amitsur [3] (generalized by Brown and McCoy [6]); the radical $\mathfrak{N}(R)$ of Section 37 by Smiley [1]. Finally, let us emphasize that these references to the radical concept for rings, as well as for other algebraic systems, are by no means complete or up-to-date.

7.29 Exercises

5. Apply Theorems 6.22, 5.44, and 7.3, and observe that a complete direct sum of regular rings is a regular ring.

References

Albert, A. A.
[1] *Structure of Algebras*, Amer. Math. Soc. Colloq. Pub., vol. 24, New York, 1939.

Amitsur, S. A.
[1] *A general theory of radicals*, I., Amer. J. Math. 74 (1952), 774–786.
[2] *A general theory of radicals*, II., Amer. J. Math. 76 (1954), 100–125.
[3] *A general theory of radicals*, III., Amer. J. Math. 76 (1954), 126–136.
[4] *Radicals of polynomial rings*, Canad. J. Math. 8 (1956), 355–361.

Artin, E.
[1] *Zur Theorie der hyperkomplexen Zahlen*, Abh. Math. Sem. Univ. Hamburg 5 (1927), 251–260.
[2] *The influence of J. H. M. Wedderburn on the development of modern algebra*, Bull. Amer. Math. Soc. 56 (1950), 65–72.

Artin, E., Nesbitt, C. J., and Thrall, R. M.
[1] *Rings with Minimum Condition*, Univ. of Mich., 1944.

Baer, R.
[1] *Radical ideals*, Amer. J. Math. 65 (1943), 537–568.

Behrens, E. A.
[1] *Nichtassoziative Ringe*, Math. Ann. 127 (1954), 441–452.

Birkhoff, G.
[1] *Subdirect unions in universal algebra*, Bull. Amer. Math. Soc. 50 (1944), 764–768.
[2] *Lattice Theory* (rev. ed.), Amer. Math. Soc. Colloq. Pub., vol. 25, New York, 1948.

Birkhoff, G. and MacLane, S.
[1] *A Survey of Modern Algebra* (rev. ed.), New York, 1953.

Bitzer, C. W.
[1] *Inverses in rings with unity*, Amer. Math. Monthly 70 (1963), 315.

Brown, B.
[1] *An extension of the Jacobson radical*, Proc. Amer. Math. 2 (1951), 114–117.

Brown, B. and McCoy, N. H.
[1] *Rings with unit element which contain a given ring*, Duke Math. J. 13 (1946), 9–20.
[2] *Radicals and subdirect sums*, Amer. J. Math. 69 (1947), 46–58.
[3] *The radical of a ring*, Duke Math. J. 15 (1948), 495–499.
[4] *The maximal regular ideal of a ring*, Proc. Amer. Math. Soc. 1 (1950), 165–171.
[5] *Some theorems on groups with applications to ring theory*, Trans. Amer. Math. Soc. 69 (1950), 302–311.

[6] *Prime ideals in nonassociative rings*, Trans. Amer. Math. Soc. 89 (1958), 245–255.

Dieudonné, J.
[1] *Sur le socle d'un anneau et les anneaux simples infinis*, Bull, Soc. Math. France 70 (1942), 46–75.

Divinsky, N.
[1] *Commutative subdirectly irreducible rings*, Proc. Amer. Math. Soc. 8 (1957), 642–648.

Goldie, A. W.
[1] *The structure of prime rings under ascending chain conditions*, Proc. London Math. Soc. (3) 8 (1958), 589–608.

Herstein, I. N.
[1] *Wedderburn's theorem and a theorem of Jacobson*, Amer. Math. Monthly 68 (1961), 249–251.

Hopkins, C.
[1] *Rings with minimal conditions for left ideals*, Ann. of Math. 40 (1939), 712–730.

Jacobson, N.
[1] *The Theory of Rings*, Amer. Math. Soc. Surveys, no. 2, New York, 1943.
[2] *Structure theory of simple rings without finiteness assumptions*, Trans. Amer. Math. Soc. 57 (1945), 228–245.
[3] *The radical and semi-simplicity for arbitrary rings*, Amer. J. Math. 67 (1945), 300–320.
[4] *Some remarks on one-sided inverses*, Proc. Amer. Math. Soc. 1 (1950), 352–355.
[5] *Lectures in Abstract Algebra*, I. *Basic Concepts*, New York, 1951.
[6] *Lectures in Abstract Algebra*, II. *Linear Algebra*, New York, 1953.
[7] *Structure of Rings*, Amer. Math. Soc. Colloq. Pub., vol. 37, Providence, 1956.

Johnson, R. E.
[1] *Representations of prime rings*, Trans. Amer. Math. Soc. 74 (1953), 351–357.
[2] *Semi-prime rings*, Trans. Amer. Math. Soc. 76 (1954), 375–388.

Johnson, R. E. and Kiokemeister, F.
[1] *The endomorphisms of the total operator domain of an infinite module*, Trans. Amer. Math. Soc. 62 (1947), 404–430.

Krull, W.
[1] *Idealtheorie in Ringen ohne Endlichkeitsbedingung*, Math. Ann. 101 (1929), 729–744.

Levitzki, J.
[1] *On the radical of a general ring*, Bull. Amer. Math. Soc. 49 (1943), 462–466.
[2] *Prime ideals and the lower radical*, Amer. J. Math. 73 (1951), 25–29.

Macduffee, C. C.
[1] *An Introduction to Abstract Algebra*, New York, 1940.

Malcev, A.
[1] *On the immersion of an algebraic ring into a field*, Math. Ann. 113 (1937), 686–691.

McCoy, N. H.
  [1] *Subdirectly irreducible commutative rings*, Duke Math. J. 12 (1945),
       381–387.
  [2] *Subdirect sums of rings*, Bull. Amer. Math. Soc. 53 (1947), 856–877.
  [3] *Rings and Ideals*, Carus Monograph No. 8, Buffalo, N.Y., 1948.
  [4] *Prime ideals in general rings*, Amer. J. Math. 71 (1949), 823–833.
  [5] *The prime radical of a polynomial ring*, Pub. Math. Debrecen 4
       (1956), 161–162.
  [6] *Introduction to Modern Algebra*, Boston, 1960.

McCoy, N. H. and Montgomery, D.
  [1] *A representation of generalized Boolean rings*, Duke Math. J. 3
       (1937), 455–459.

Miller, K. S.
  [1] *Elements of Modern Abstract Algebra*, New York, 1958.

Moore, J. T.
  [1] *Elements of Abstract Algebra*, New York, 1962.

Nagata, M.
  [1] *On the theory of radicals in a ring*, J. Math. Soc. Japan 3 (1951),
       330–344.

von Neumann, J.
  [1] *On regular rings*, Proc. Nat. Acad. Sci. 22 (1936), 707–713.

Ore, O.
  [1] *Linear equations in non-commutative fields*, Ann. of Math. 32 (1931),
       463–477.

Perlis, S.
  [1] *A characterization of the radical of an algebra*, Bull. Amer. Math.
       Soc. 48 (1942), 128–132.

Segal, I. E.
  [1] *The group algebra of a locally compact group*, Trans. Amer. Math.
       Soc. 61 (1947), 69–105.

Smiley, M. F.
  [1] *Application of a radical of Brown and McCoy to non-associative rings*,
       Amer. J. Math. 72 (1950), 93–100.

Stone, M. H.
  [1] *The theory of representations for Boolean algebras*, Trans. Amer.
       Math. Soc. 40 (1936), 37–111.

Utumi, Y.
  [1] *A theorem of Levitzki*, Amer. Math. Monthly 70 (1963), 286.

van der Waerden, B. L.
  [1] *Modern Algebra*, vol. 1, New York, 1949.
  [2] *Modern Algebra*, vol. 2, New York, 1950.

Wedderburn, J. H. M.
  [1] *A theorem on finite algebras*, Trans. Amer. Math. Soc. 6 (1905),
       349–352.
  [2] *On hypercomplex numbers*, Proc. London Math. Soc. (2) 6 (1908),
       77–117.

Zariski, O. and Samuel, P.
  [1] *Commutative Algebra*, vol. 1, Princeton, N.J., 1958.
  [2] *Commutative Algebra*, vol. 2, Princeton, N.J., 1960.

Index

A

Addition, 1
  of ideals, 27
  of subspaces, 92
Additive group of a ring, 2
Additive inverse, 1
Algebra, 10
  of matrices, 11
  of quaternions, 14
Annihilating right ideal, 100
Annihilating subspace, 100
Anti-isomorphism, 83, 101
Ascending chain condition (a.c.c.),
  36
Associative laws, 1, 2

B

Basis of an ideal, 28
  of a vector space, 92
Boolean ring, 10

C

Center, 8
Centralizer, 90
Characteristic, 4

Commutative law, 1
Commutative ring, 2
Complete direct sum, 19, 50
Complete matrix ring, 14
Component rings of direct sum, 18

D

Dense ring, 95
Descending chain condition (d.c.c.),
  35
Difference group, 41
Dimension of vector space, 93
Direct sum of rings, 18
  of ideals, 28
Discrete direct sum, 19, 50
Distributive laws, 2
Division ring, 6
Divisor of zero, 4

E

Endomorphism, 75